Macmillan McGraw-Hill

California Mathematics 2

Reteach and Skills Practice Workbook

TO THE TEACHER These worksheets are the same ones found in the Chapter Resource Masters for *California Mathematics, Grade 2*. The answers to these worksheets are available at the end of each Chapter Resource Masters booklet.

The McGraw·Hill Companies

Send all inquiries to:
Macmillan/McGraw-Hill
8787 Orion Place
Columbus, OH 43240

SBN: 978-0-02-106344-4
MHID: 0-02-106344-3 *Reteach and Skills Practice Workbook, Grade 2*

Printed in the United States of America.

2 3 4 5 6 7 8 9 10 079 14 13 12 11 10 09 08

CONTENTS

Chapter 8 Multiplication and Division Concepts

Chapter 9 Fractions

Chapter 10 Numbers to 1,000

Chapter 11 Geometry

Chapter 12 Measurement and Time

Chapter 13 Three-Digit Addition

Chapter 14 Three-Digit Subtraction

1-1

Name ______________________________

Reteach

2NS1.2, 2MR1.2

Tens and Ones

Chapter Resources

Another name for ten ones is one ten.

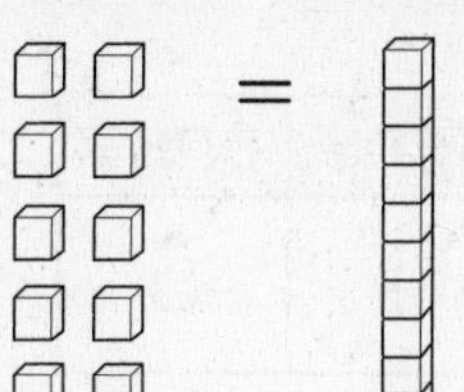

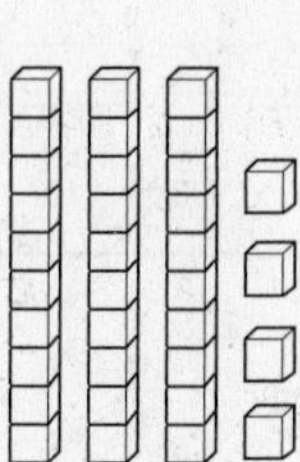

tens	ones
3	4

3 tens 4 ones = 34 in all

Count how many tens and ones. Write the number.

1. 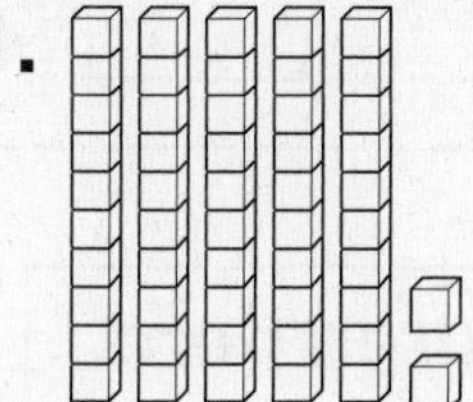

tens	ones
5	2

______ tens ______ ones = ______ in all

2. 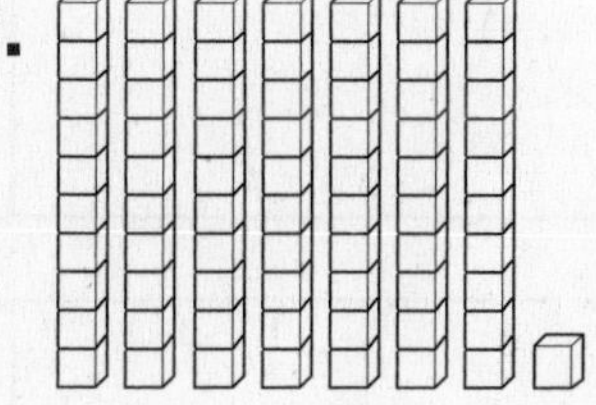

tens	ones

______ tens ______ ones = ______ in all

3. 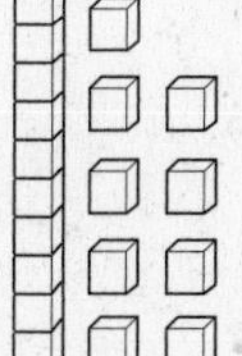

tens	ones

______ tens ______ ones = ______ in all

Name ______________________________

1-1

Skills Practice

2NS1.2, 2MR1.2

Write how many ones. Then write how many tens.

1. 15 = __1__ ten __5__ ones

__10__ + __5__ = __15__

tens	ones
1	5

2. 43 = ______ tens ______ ones

______ + ______ = ______

tens	ones

3. 66 = ______ tens ______ ones

______ + ______ = ______

tens	ones

Draw a picture to solve.

4. There are 10 pencils in a box.
Deb buys 3 boxes.
How many pencils will she have?

______ pencils

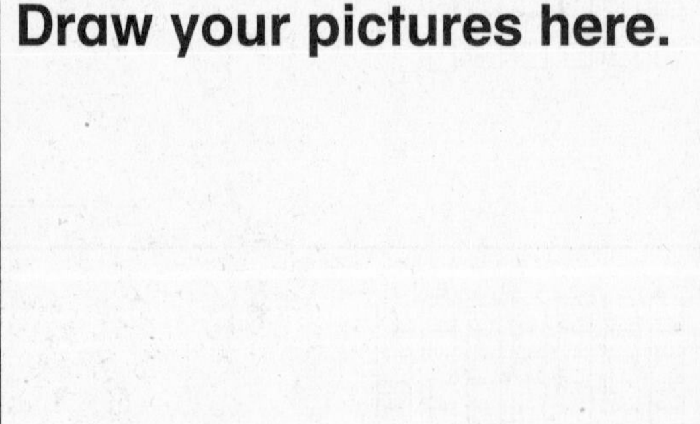

5. Juan buys 2 boxes of apples.
Each box has 10 apples.
Juan buys 4 more apples.
How many apples will Juan have in all?

______ apples

Name ______________________________

1-2

Reteach

2NS1.1

Place Value to 100

Chapter Resources

Each digit in a number has a value.

= 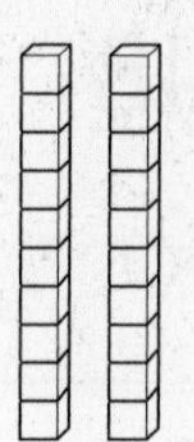 +

27 = 2 tens + 7 ones

= 20 + 7

Circle the value of the underlined digit.

1. 32

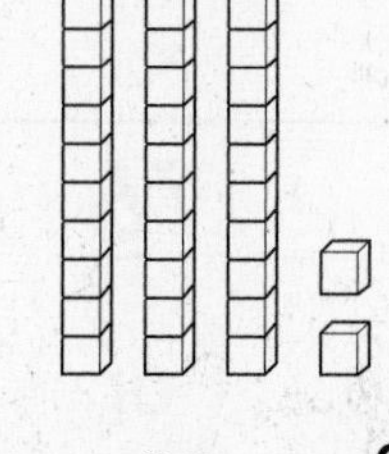

3 or 30

2. 45

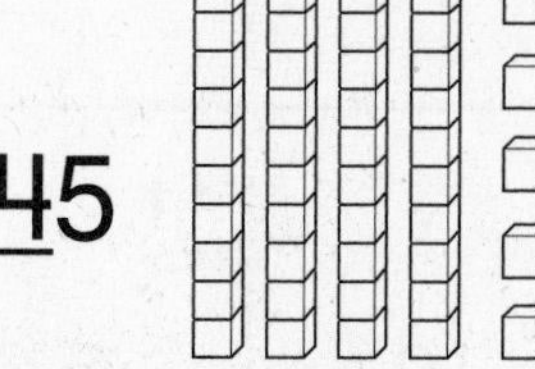

4 or 40

3. 63

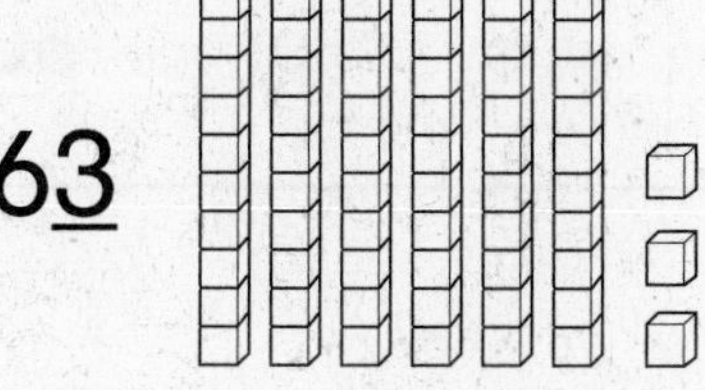

3 or 30

4. 51

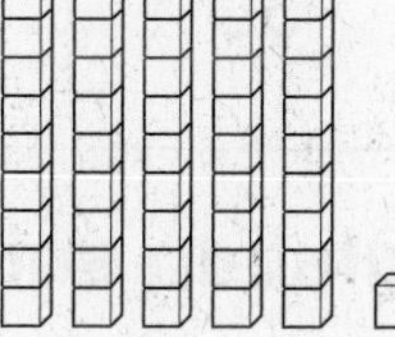

5 or 50

5. 49

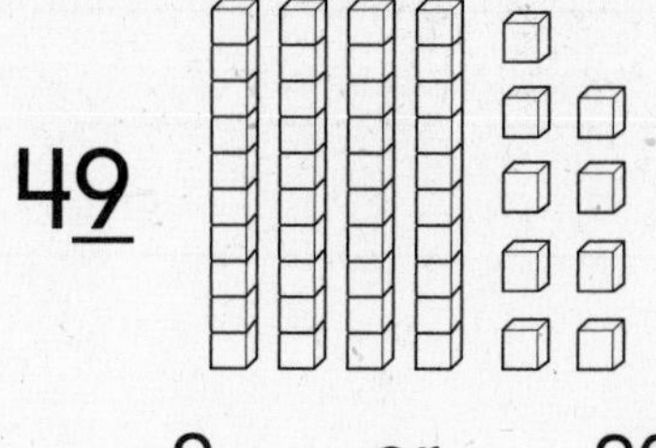

9 or 90

6. 18

1 or 10

Name ______________________________

1-2

Skills Practice

2NS1.1

Place Value to 100

Circle the value of the underlined digit.

1. 63 (underlined: 6) 6 or 60	**2.** 48 (underlined: 8) 8 or 80	**3.** 19 (underlined: 1) 1 or 10
4. 86 (underlined: 8) 8 or 80	**5.** 27 (underlined: 7) 7 or 70	**6.** 71 (underlined: 7) 7 or 70
7. 59 (underlined: 9) 9 or 90	**8.** 15 (underlined: 5) 5 or 50	**9.** 93 (underlined: 9) 9 or 90
10. 41 (underlined: 1) 1 or 10	**11.** 52 (underlined: 5) 5 or 50	**12.** 76 (underlined: 6) 6 or 60
13. 31 (underlined: 3) 3 or 30	**14.** 29 (underlined: 2) 2 or 20	**15.** 65 (underlined: 5) 5 or 50

Use place value to solve.

16. Kai has 59 pennies.
A drink costs 69 pennies.
Does he have enough to
buy the water?
How do you know?

____

____

____

____

Name ______________________________

1-3

Reteach (1)

2NS1.0, 2MR1.1

Problem-Solving Strategy: Logical Reasoning

Chapter Resources

Three boys ride bicycles.
Pat rides behind Bill.
Bill rides behind Rob.
Who rides in front?

Step 1
Understand

What do I know?

Pat rides behind Bill.

Bill rides behind Rob.

What do I need to find?

I need to find ____________________.

Step 2
Plan

How will I find the answer?
I can use logical reasoning.

Step 3
Solve

Use logical reasoning.

The first clue: Pat is behind Bill.

Write the order. __________, __________

The second clue: Bill is behind Rob.

Write the order. __________, __________

Who rides in front? __________

Step 4
Check

Does my answer make sense? Yes No

I-3

Name ______________________________

Reteach (2)

2NS1.0, 2MR1.1

Problem-Solving Strategy: Logical Reasoning

Use logical reasoning to solve.

Show your work here.

1. Kris, Nick, and Lara share a bus seat. Kris sits by the window. Lara is not sitting next to Kris. Who sits in the middle?

____

2. Tim, Emma, Ling, and Cory run a race. Emma is first. Ling is after Tim. Tim is not second. Who is second?

____

3. Pete, Ed, and Jane buy ice cream. Their cones have 1, 2, and 3 scoops. Pete has 2 scoops. Ed has more scoops than Pete. How many scoops does Jane have?

______ scoop

4. Juan, Mia, and Wes pick 3 cards. Their numbers are 8, 5, and 1. Juan picks number 5. Wes does not pick number 8. Who picks number 8?

____

Name ______________________________

1-3

Skills Practice

2NS1.0, 2MR1.1

Problem-Solving Strategy: Logical Reasoning

Chapter Resources

Use *logical reasoning* to solve. | **Show your work here.**

1. Zach, Alex, and Jen are on stage. Zach is on the left. Jen is not next to Zach. Who is in the middle?

   ____

2. Lori, Sara, Jill, and Ann are in line. Lori is first. Sara is after Lori. Ann is before Jill. Who is fourth?

   ____

3. Muhammed, Maria, and Chan have tickets. They are numbered 1, 2, and 3. Maria has number 2. Chan does not have number 3. Who has number 3?

   ____

4. Faye, Dan, and Trey are wearing soccer shirts. The shirts are numbered 2, 6, and 7. Dan has number 6. Trey's number is greater than Dan's. Who has number 2?

   ____

1-4

Name ______________________

Reteach

2NS1.1, 2NS1.2

Read and Write Numbers

Chapter Resources

You can write word names for numbers.

1	one	**11**	eleven	**30**	thirty
2	two	**12**	twelve	**40**	forty
3	three	**13**	thirteen	**50**	fifty
4	four	**14**	fourteen	**60**	sixty
5	five	**15**	fifteen	**70**	seventy
6	six	**16**	sixteen	**80**	eighty
7	seven	**17**	seventeen	**90**	ninety
8	eight	**18**	eighteen	**100**	one hundred
9	nine	**19**	nineteen		
10	ten	**20**	twenty		

Write the number and number words.

1.

17, seventeen

2. 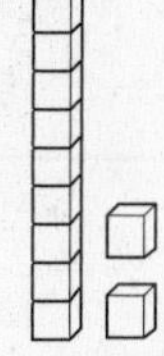

______, ______________

3. 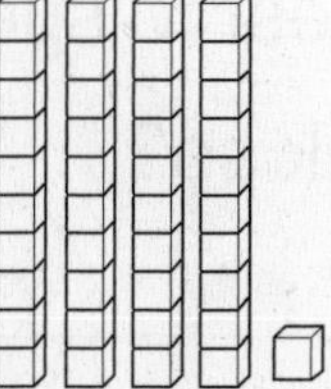

______, ______________

4. 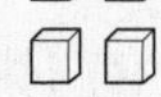

______, ______________

Name ______________________

1-4

Skills Practice

2NS1.1, 2NS1.2

Read and Write Numbers

Write the number or the number words.

1. seventy 70
2. sixteen ______
3. thirty-seven ______
4. twenty-five ______
5. eighty-nine ______
6. twelve ______
7. forty-eight ______
8. ninety-two ______
9. fifty-one ______
10. sixty-three ______
11. 23 ______________
12. 45 ______________
13. 78 ______________
14. 53 ______________
15. 13 ______________
16. 90 ______________

Solve.

17. Jamal needs to find four numbers using the digits 3 and 4. He named 3 and 34.

    Name the other two numbers.

    ____

    ____

18. Which number word do you think is the hardest to spell?

    Why do you think so?

    ____

    ____

Name ______________________

1-5

Reteach

2NS6.0

Estimate Numbers

Count to get an exact number.

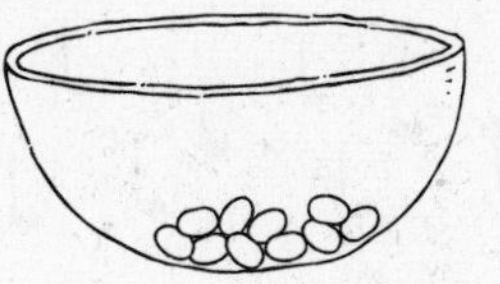

______ grapes

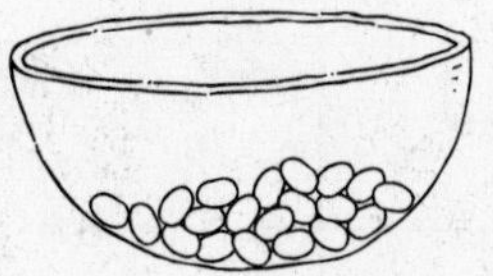

______ grapes

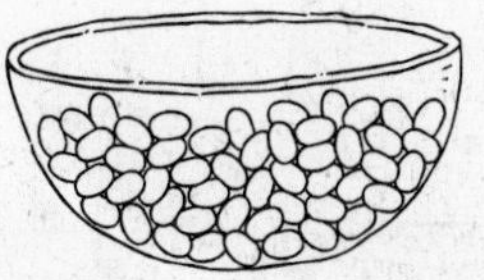

50 grapes

Make your estimate. Use the jars to help.
Circle your answer.

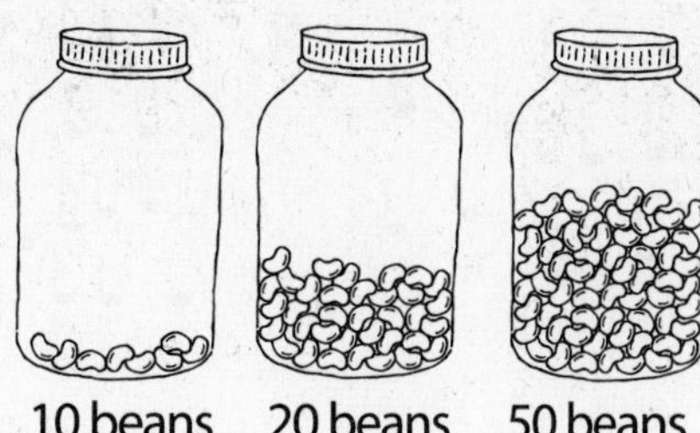

1\. 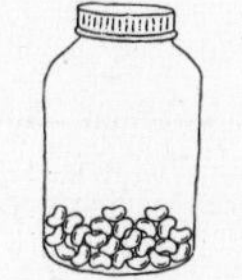

about 10 about 20

2\. 

about 10 about 50

3\. 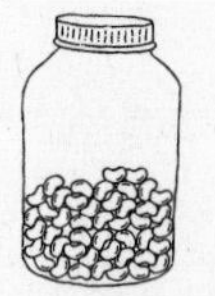

about 20 about 50

4\. 

about 10 about 20

5\. 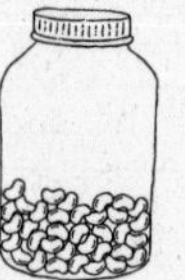

about 10 about 50

6\. 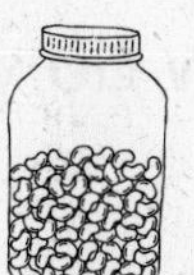

about 20 about 50

Name ______________________________

1-5

Skills Practice

2NS6.0

Estimate Numbers

Estimate. Circle your answer.

1.

about 20 about 50

2.

about 10 about 60

3.

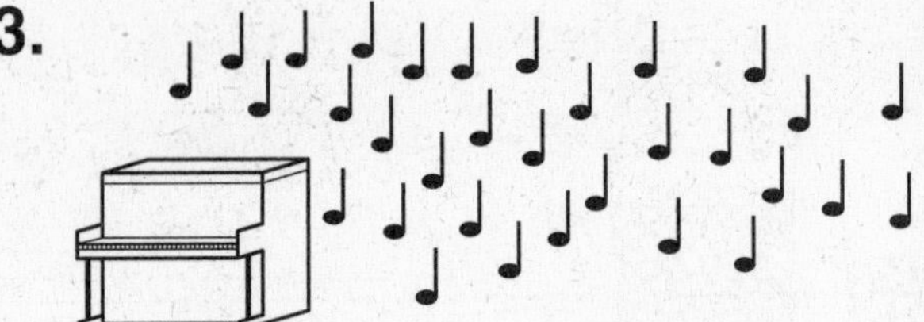

about 30 about 80

4.

about 10 about 50

Estimate to solve.

5. Mr. Green orders 48 horns for the band. The band has five different sections. Two sections have 10 children. Three sections have more than 10 children. Is there a horn for every child in the band? How do you know?

____

____

____

____

____

____

____

Name ______________________________

1-6

Reteach

2NS1.3

Order Numbers

Chapter Resources

The hundred chart gives the numbers 1 to 100 in order.

1	2	3	4	5	6	7	8	9	10
11	12	13	14	15	16	17	18	19	20
21	22	23	24	25	26	27	28	29	30
31	32	33	34	35	36	37	38	39	40
41	42	43	44	45	46	47	48	49	50
51	52	53	54	55	56	57	58	59	60
61	62	63	64	65	66	67	68	69	70
71	72	73	74	75	76	77	78	79	80
81	82	83	84	85	86	87	88	89	90
91	92	93	94	95	96	97	98	99	100

22 comes just *before* 23

25 comes *between* 24 and 26

29 comes just *after* 28

Use the chart to help you answer.
Write the number that comes:

	just before	just after	between
1.	42 43	49, 50	43, 44 45
2.	______ 45	51, ______	47, ______ 49
3.	______ 71	72, ______	74, ______ 76
4.	______ 77	88, ______	90, ______ 92

Circle the correct words.

5. 26 comes ____________ 27

just before
just after
between

6. 28 comes ____________ 27

just before
just after
between

Name ______________________________

1-6

Skills Practice

2NS1.3

Order Numbers

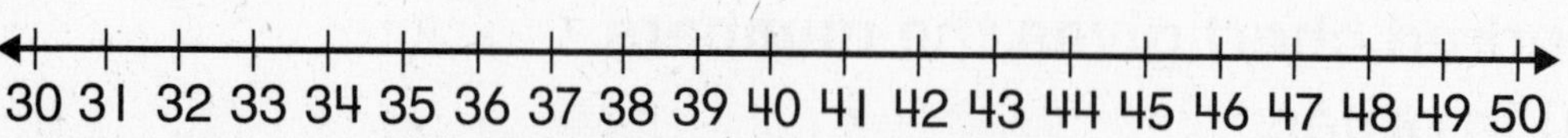

Use the number line to fill in the blanks.

1. 33, 34, 35	43, ______, 45	34, 35, ______
2. ______, 39, 40	45, 46, ______	37, ______, 39
3. 39, ______, 41	47, 48, ______	______, 46, 47
4. 48, 49, ______	29, ______, 31	______, 38, 39

5. ______, 38, 39, ______	______, 31, 32, ______
6. ______, 44, ______, 46	40, ______, ______, 43
7. 37, 38, ______, ______	______, 39, ______, 41
8. 46, ______, ______, 49	34, 35, ______, ______

Use number order to solve.

9. Cindy drops her notebook.
She picked up pages 28, 29,
32, 33, 34, and 35.

Which pages are missing?

____

Name ______________________

1-8 Reteach

2SDAP2.1, 2SDAP2.2

Patterns

Chapter Resources

You can use patterns to solve problems.
Some patterns are *repeating patterns*.

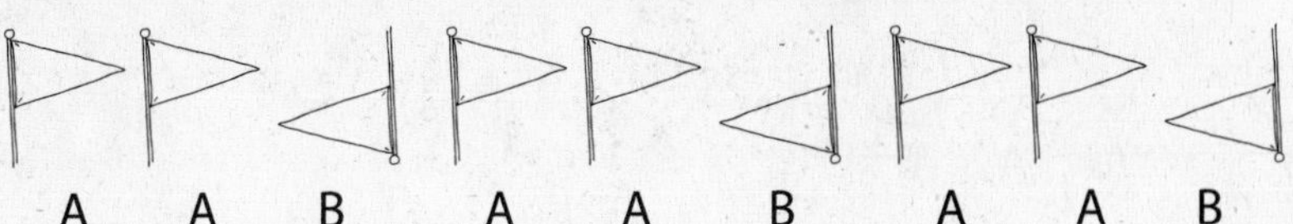

A A B A A B A A B

A A B

Some patterns are *growing patterns*.

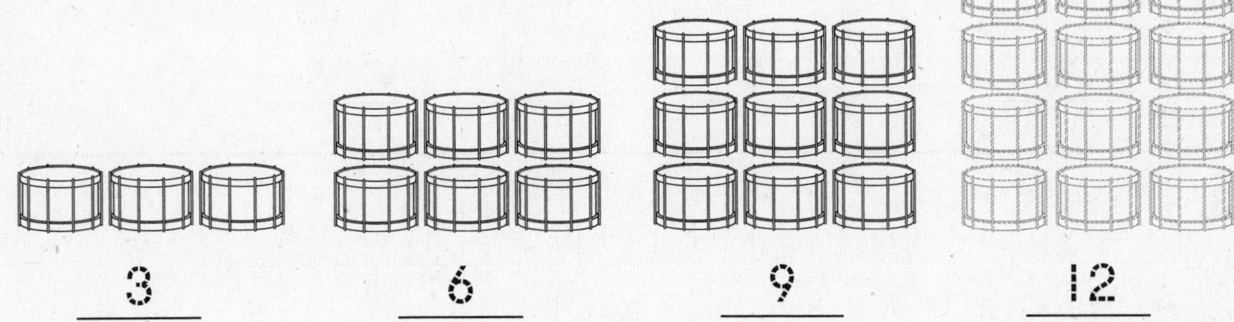

3 6 9 12

Draw a picture to continue each pattern.

1. ☆☆☆○ ☆☆☆○ ☆☆☆○ ☆ ☆ ☆ ○

A A A B A A A B A A A B

____ ____ ____ ____

2. ⇧⇩⇩ ⇧⇩⇩ ⇧⇩⇩

A B B A B B A B B

____ ____ ____

3.

2 4 6 ____

Name ______________________

1-8

Skills Practice

2SDAP2.1, 2SDAP2.2

Patterns

Draw a picture to continue the pattern.

1. 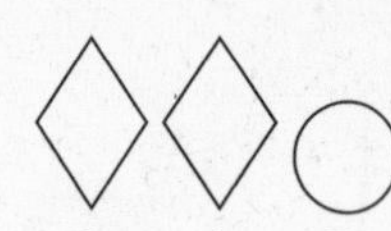 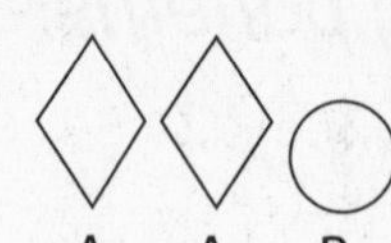

A A B A A B A A B

A A B

2.  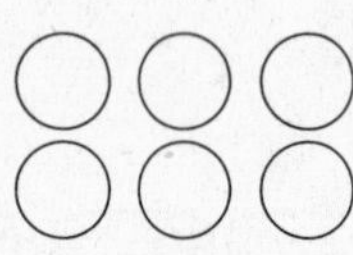 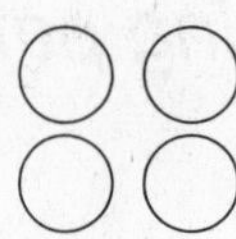

8 6 4 ______

3. 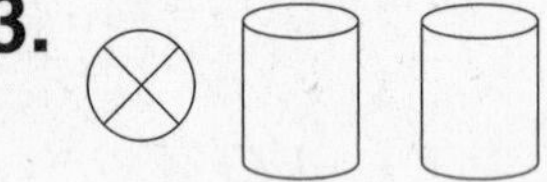

A B B A B B A B B

______ ______ ______

4.  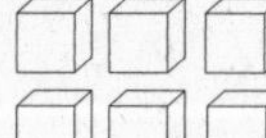  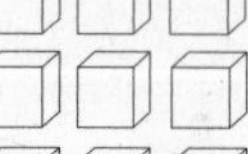

______ ______ ______ ______

Solve.

5. Owen paints this border on his picture: star, star, moon. How can he use letters to show his pattern?

______

6. Kat is building this block pattern: 2 blocks, 4 blocks, 6 blocks. How many blocks should Kat build next?

______ blocks

Name ______________________________

1-9

Reteach (1)

2MR1.1, 2NS2.2

Problem-Solving Investigation: Choose a Strategy

There are 20 children on the playground.
Eleven children play kickball.
Five children play hopscotch.
The rest play soccer.

How many children play soccer?

Step 1
Read

What do I know?

There are __20__ children on the playground.

__11__ play kickball.

__5__ play hopscotch.

What do I need to find?

How many play __soccer__.

Step 2
Plan

How will I find how many?

I can __act it out__.

Step 3
Solve

I can use counters to act it out.

______ ______ ______

Step 4
Check

Did I act it out? ______

Does my answer make sense? ______

Name ______________________________

1-9

Reteach (2)

2MR1.1, 2NS2.2

Problem-Solving Investigation: Choose a Strategy

Problem-Solving Strategies
Draw a Picture
Logical Reasoning
Act it Out

Solve.

Show your work here.

1. Mandy makes 4 snowballs. Sara makes 2 snowballs. How many snowballs do they have in all?

__________ snowballs

2. Four kids wait in line to use the slide. Chad is third in line. Don is behind Chad. Al is in front of Bob. Bob is second in line. Who is first in line?

__________ is first in line.

3. Jill draws a picture for her mom. The picture has three circles. Jill starts with a blue circle. She puts a red circle next to the yellow circle. She puts a yellow circle next to the blue circle. Which color is the middle circle?

____

Name ____________________

Skills Practice

2MR1.1, 2NS2.2

Problem-Solving Investigation: Choose a Strategy

Problem-Solving Strategies
Draw a Picture
Logical Reasoning
Act it Out

Solve.

Show your work here.

1. Kyra is feeding eight ducks. Five ducks swim away. How many ducks are left for Kyra to feed?

   ______ ducks are left

2. Dex does a silly walk. His walk is step, hop, hop, step, hop, hop. How could Dex use A's and B's to show the pattern of his silly walk?

   ____

3. Three children are in line to play kickball. Kim is not second. Cedric will kick after Bob. Bob is not first. In what order will they kick?

   ____

Name ______________________________

1-10

Reteach

2SDAP2.1, 2SDAP2.2

Patterns on a Hundred Chart

Skip counting on a hundred chart makes patterns.

What is the pattern shown? ______________________

1	2	3	4	5	6	7	8	9	10
11	12	13	14	15	16	17	18	19	20
21	22	23	24	25	26	27	28	29	30
31	32	33	34	35	36	37	38	39	40
41	42	43	44	45	46	47	48	49	50
51	52	53	54	55	56	57	58	59	60
61	62	63	64	65	66	67	68	69	70
71	72	73	74	75	76	77	78	79	80
81	82	83	84	85	86	87	88	89	90
91	92	93	94	95	96	97	98	99	100

Use a hundred chart to skip count.

1. Start at 1. Skip count by 4. Color.
2. Start at 1. Skip count by 5. Color a different color.
3. Tell what patterns you see in the chart.

____

____

____

1	2	3	4	5	6	7	8	9	10
11	12	13	14	15	16	17	18	19	20
21	22	23	24	25	26	27	28	29	30
31	32	33	34	35	36	37	38	39	40
41	42	43	44	45	46	47	48	49	50
51	52	53	54	55	56	57	58	59	60
61	62	63	64	65	66	67	68	69	70
71	72	73	74	75	76	77	78	79	80
81	82	83	84	85	86	87	88	89	90
91	92	93	94	95	96	97	98	99	100

Name ______________________________

1-10

Skills Practice

Patterns on a Hundred Chart

Use the hundred chart to skip count.

1	2	3	4	5	6	7	8	9	10
11	12	13	14	15	16	17	18	19	20
21	22	23	24	25	26	27	28	29	30
31	32	33	34	35	36	37	38	39	40
41	42	43	44	45	46	47	48	49	50
51	52	53	54	55	56	57	58	59	60
61	62	63	64	65	66	67	68	69	70
71	72	73	74	75	76	77	78	79	80
81	82	83	84	85	86	87	88	89	90
91	92	93	94	95	96	97	98	99	100

1. Skip count by 3s.

30, 33, 36, ______, ______, ______, ______.

2. Skip count by 6s.

24, 30, 36, ______, ______, ______, ______.

3. Skip count by 9s.

18, 27, 36, ______, ______, ______, ______.

Use a number pattern to solve.

4. Clint has to make shoes for 16 horses. How many shoes will he make?

______

5. Kayla sees seven spiders in her garden. Each spider has 8 legs.

How many legs does she see?

______

6. Erika has to name the pattern on the number chart.

What should Erika call this pattern?

____

1	2	3	4	5	6	7	8	9	10
11	12	13	14	15	16	17	18	19	20
21	22	23	24	25	26	27	28	29	30
31	32	33	34	35	36	37	38	39	40
41	42	43	44	45	46	47	48	49	50
51	52	53	54	55	56	57	58	59	60
61	62	63	64	65	66	67	68	69	70
71	72	73	74	75	76	77	78	79	80
81	82	83	84	85	86	87	88	89	90
91	92	93	94	95	96	97	98	99	100

Name ______________________

2-1

Reteach

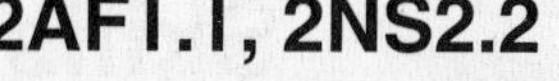

Addition Properties

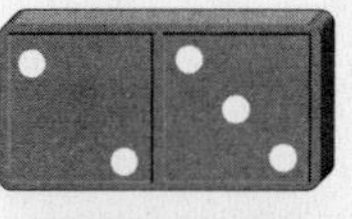

2 + 3 = 5

3 + 2 = 5

The order of the addends is changed. The sum is the same.

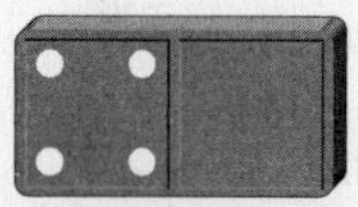

4 + 0 = 4

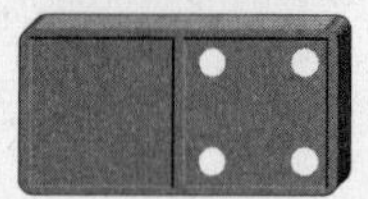

0 + 4 = 4

Add 0 to a number. The sum is the same as the other addend.

Find each sum.

1. 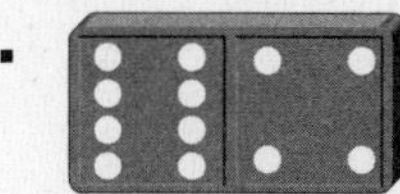

8 + 4 = 12

4 + 8 = 12

2. 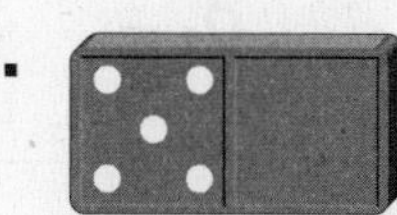

5 + 0 = ______

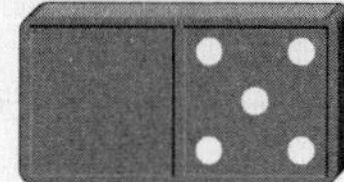

0 + 5 = ______

3. 

3 + 4 = ______

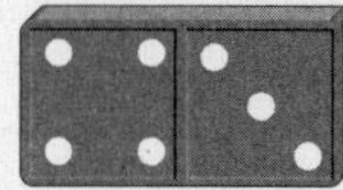

4 + 3 = ______

4. 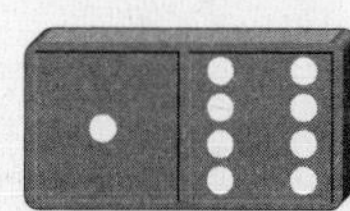

1 + 8 = ______

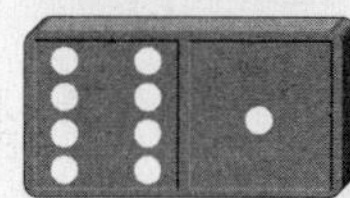

8 + 1 = ______

5. 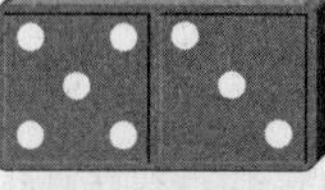

5 + 3 = ______

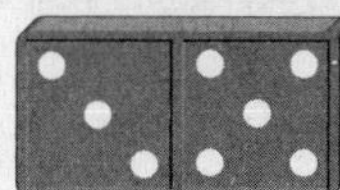

3 + 5 = ______

6. 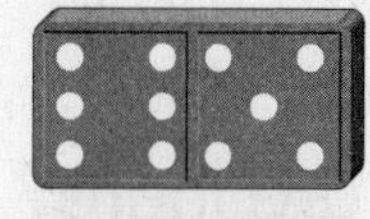

6 + 5 = ______

5 + 6 = ______

Name ______________________________

2-1

Skills Practice

Addition Properties

2AF1.1, 2NS2.2

Find each sum.

1. $\begin{array}{r} 3 \\ +2 \\ \hline 5 \end{array}$ $\begin{array}{r} 2 \\ +3 \\ \hline \end{array}$

2. $\begin{array}{r} 5 \\ +7 \\ \hline \end{array}$ $\begin{array}{r} 7 \\ +5 \\ \hline \end{array}$

3. $\begin{array}{r} 2 \\ +0 \\ \hline \end{array}$ $\begin{array}{r} 0 \\ +2 \\ \hline \end{array}$

4. $\begin{array}{r} 4 \\ +5 \\ \hline \end{array}$ $\begin{array}{r} 5 \\ +4 \\ \hline \end{array}$

5. $\begin{array}{r} 7 \\ +0 \\ \hline \end{array}$ $\begin{array}{r} 0 \\ +7 \\ \hline \end{array}$

6. $\begin{array}{r} 4 \\ +2 \\ \hline \end{array}$ $\begin{array}{r} 2 \\ +4 \\ \hline \end{array}$

7. $\begin{array}{r} 5 \\ +6 \\ \hline \end{array}$ $\begin{array}{r} 6 \\ +5 \\ \hline \end{array}$

8. $\begin{array}{r} 3 \\ +4 \\ \hline \end{array}$ $\begin{array}{r} 4 \\ +3 \\ \hline \end{array}$

9. $\begin{array}{r} 7 \\ +4 \\ \hline \end{array}$ $\begin{array}{r} 4 \\ +7 \\ \hline \end{array}$

10. $\begin{array}{r} 7 \\ +2 \\ \hline \end{array}$ $\begin{array}{r} 2 \\ +7 \\ \hline \end{array}$

11. $\begin{array}{r} 0 \\ +3 \\ \hline \end{array}$ $\begin{array}{r} 3 \\ +0 \\ \hline \end{array}$

12. $\begin{array}{r} 4 \\ +6 \\ \hline \end{array}$ $\begin{array}{r} 6 \\ +4 \\ \hline \end{array}$

13. 8 + 3 = ______

3 + 8 = ______

14. 6 + 4 = ______

4 + 6 = ______

15. 3 + 9 = ______

9 + 3 = ______

Solve.

16. There are 2 brown frogs.
There are 8 green frogs.
How many frogs are there?

______ frogs

17. There are 8 spotted turtles.
There are 2 striped turtles.
How many turtles are there?

______ turtles

Name ______________________

2-2

Reteach

2NS2.2

Count On to Add

Chapter Resources

You can use squares to count on.

Find 5 + 3. Start at 5. Count on 3.

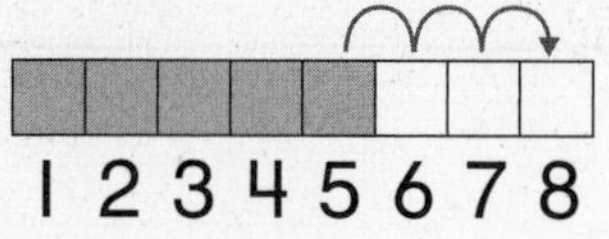

5 + 3 = 8

$$\begin{array}{r} 5 \\ +\ 3 \\ \hline 8 \end{array}$$

Use the squares. Add squares to count on.

1. 8 + 1 = 9

2. 6 + 2 = ______

3. 7 + 3 = ______

4. 5 + 1 = ______

5. 9 + 3 = ______

6. 7 + 2 = ______

7. 6 + 3 = ______

Name ______________________________

2-2

Skills Practice

2NS2.2

Count On to Add

You can use a number line to add.

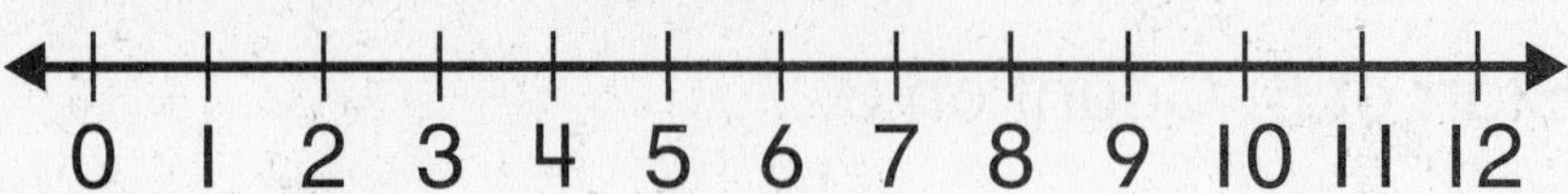

Use the number line. Count on to add.

1. 6 + 1 = 7   2 + 3 = ____   4 + 3 = ____

2. 1 + 7 = ____   5 + 2 = ____   6 + 3 = ____

3. $\begin{array}{r}3\\+9\\\hline\end{array}$ $\begin{array}{r}4\\+3\\\hline\end{array}$ $\begin{array}{r}7\\+2\\\hline\end{array}$ $\begin{array}{r}1\\+6\\\hline\end{array}$ $\begin{array}{r}5\\+0\\\hline\end{array}$ $\begin{array}{r}2\\+2\\\hline\end{array}$

4. $\begin{array}{r}8\\+3\\\hline\end{array}$ $\begin{array}{r}2\\+3\\\hline\end{array}$ $\begin{array}{r}2\\+6\\\hline\end{array}$ $\begin{array}{r}5\\+1\\\hline\end{array}$ $\begin{array}{r}6\\+3\\\hline\end{array}$ $\begin{array}{r}0\\+4\\\hline\end{array}$

5. $\begin{array}{r}7\\+3\\\hline\end{array}$ $\begin{array}{r}1\\+9\\\hline\end{array}$ $\begin{array}{r}8\\+0\\\hline\end{array}$ $\begin{array}{r}4\\+2\\\hline\end{array}$ $\begin{array}{r}9\\+2\\\hline\end{array}$ $\begin{array}{r}3\\+7\\\hline\end{array}$

Solve.

6. A frog jumps over 6 rocks. Then he jumps over 2 more.

How many rocks does he jump over?

____ rocks

7. A turtle lays 4 eggs. Then she lays 3 more.

How many eggs does she lay in all?

____ eggs

Name ____________________

2-3

Reteach (1)

2NS2.1, 2MR2.2

Problem-Solving Strategy: Act It Out

Chapter Resources

Jeff likes to watch birds on the way to school. Today, he saw 5 crows and 12 robins. How many birds did Jeff see?

Step 1
Understand

What do I know?

Jeff saw 5 crows.

Jeff saw 12 robins.

What do I need to find out?

How many birds did Jeff see?

Step 2
Plan

How will I find how many birds he saw?

I can act it out using ____________.

Step 3
Solve

Act it out

I can use red counters to stand for robins.

I can use white counters for crows.

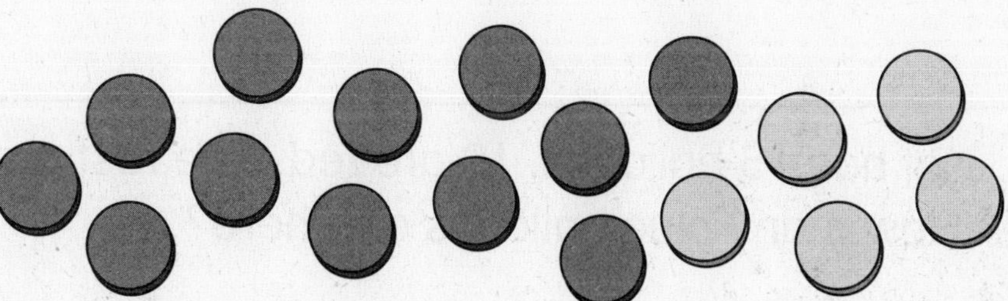

Step 4
Check

Look Back

Did I act it out? ______

Does my answer make sense? ______

2-3

Name ______________________________

Reteach (2)

2NS2.1, 2MR2.2

Problem-Solving Strategy: Act It Out

Preparation: Counters are needed for this activity.

Solve. Use counters to act it out.

1. Mary sees 1 dog, 4 bees, and 2 swans at the park.
   How many swans does she see?

   ______ swans

2. 7 cars are in the parking lot. 4 cars leave. 2 more come back.
   How many cars are there now?

   ______ cars

3. Mia saw 4 bears at the zoo. She saw 9 bears on T.V.
   How many bears did she see in all?

   ______ bears

4. Kat has 15 balloons. 10 are red. The rest are blue.
   How many blue balloons are there?

   ______ blue balloons

5. There are 4 markers in the bin. Rick puts 5 more in the bin.
   How many markers are there altogether?

   ______ markers

Name ______________________________

2-3

Skills Practice

2MR2.2

Problem-Solving Strategy: Act It Out

Preparation: Erasers or other manipulatives are needed for this activity.

Solve. Use classroom erasers to act it out.

1. Scott buys all the [bear] and [panda] erasers.
   How many erasers does he buy in all? ______________

2. Kelly buys all the [seal] erasers.
   How many erasers does she have? ______________

3. Sara buys all the [lion] erasers. Then she buys all the [whale] erasers.
   How many erasers does she have? ______________

4. Ted buys all the [zebra] and [elephant] erasers. Then he buys 8 more erasers.
   How many erasers does he have? ______________

Name ____________________

2-4

Reteach

Doubles

2NS2.2

Addends that are the same are called doubles.

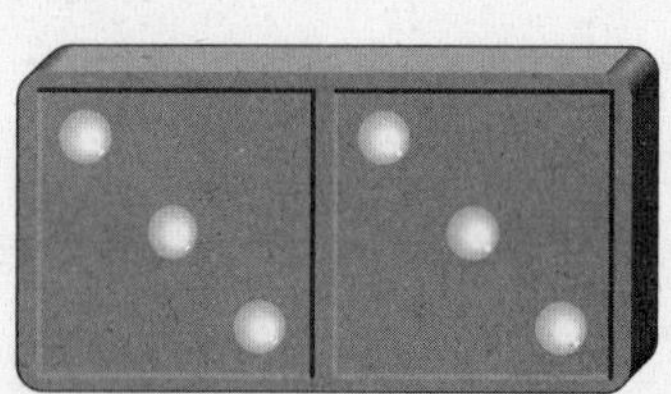

3 + 3 = 6

addend addend

Add. Use doubles.

1. 4 + 4 = 8

2. 6 + 6 = ______

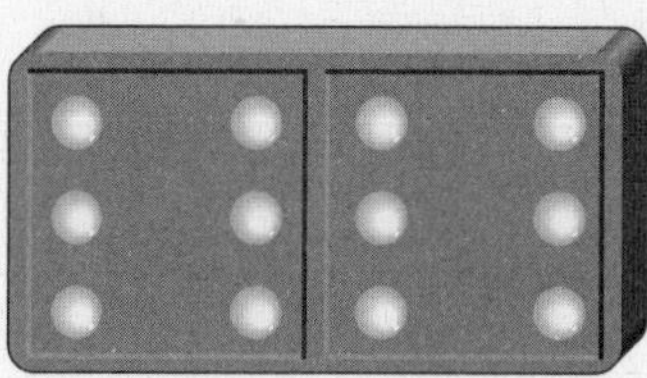

3. 2 + 2 = ______

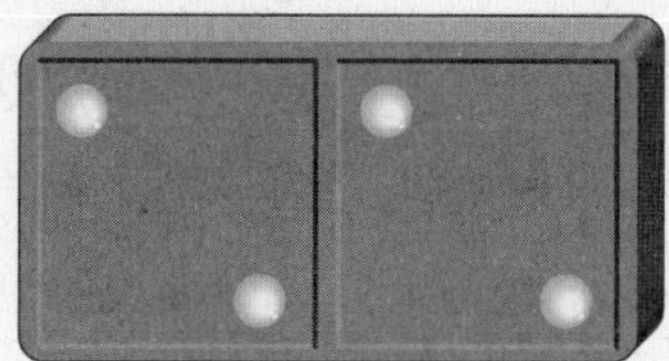

4. 5 + 5 = ______

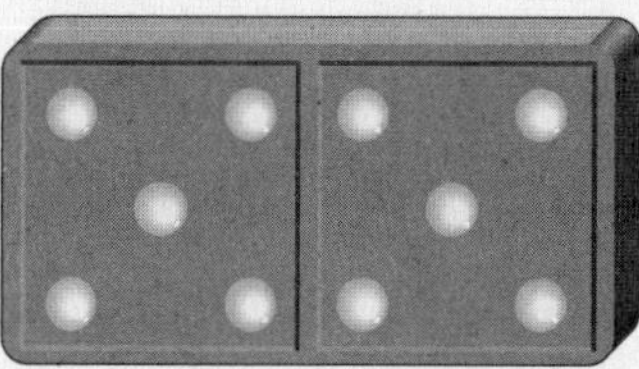

5. 7 + 7 = ______

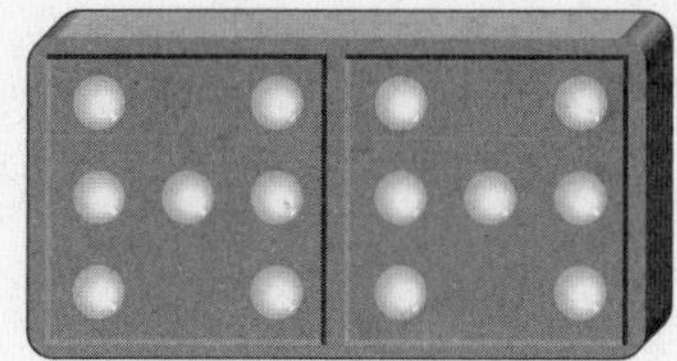

6. 9 + 9 = ______

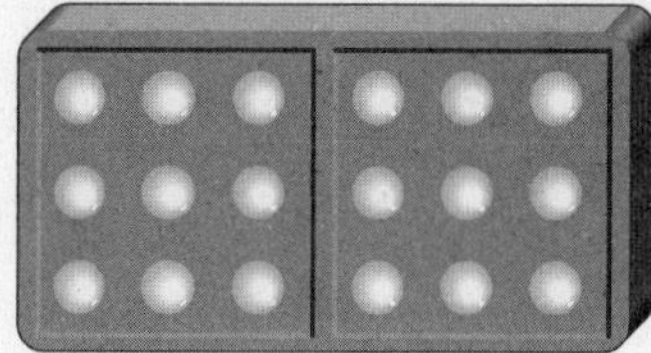

Name ______________________________

2-4

Skills Practice

2NS2.2

Doubles

Add.

1. $\begin{array}{r} 3 \\ +4 \\ \hline \end{array}$ $\begin{array}{r} 5 \\ +7 \\ \hline \end{array}$ $\begin{array}{r} 4 \\ +4 \\ \hline \end{array}$ $\begin{array}{r} 8 \\ +4 \\ \hline \end{array}$ $\begin{array}{r} 9 \\ +0 \\ \hline \end{array}$

2. $\begin{array}{r} 3 \\ +3 \\ \hline \end{array}$ $\begin{array}{r} 4 \\ +9 \\ \hline \end{array}$ $\begin{array}{r} 6 \\ +2 \\ \hline \end{array}$ $\begin{array}{r} 8 \\ +8 \\ \hline \end{array}$ $\begin{array}{r} 6 \\ +7 \\ \hline \end{array}$

3. 8 + 3 = ______ 9 + 9 = ______ 7 + 6 = ______

4. 6 + 6 = ______ 7 + 6 = ______ 7 + 7 = ______

Solve. Write the number sentence.

5. Cameron buys 6 baseball caps. Deb buys the same number of caps. How many caps do they have altogether?

______ + ______ = ______

6. Andy has 9 shirts. His brother has an equal number of shirts. How many shirts do the boys have in all?

_____ + _____ = _____ shirts

7. Circle all of the doubles facts on this page.

Name ______________________________

2-5

Reteach

2AF1.1, 2NS2.1

Near Doubles

Knowing doubles can help you learn other facts.

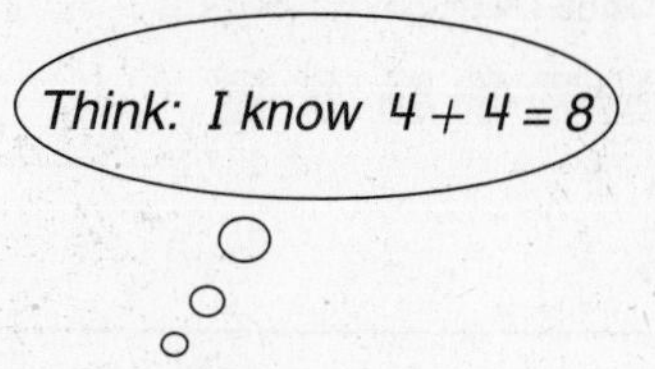

4 + 4 = 8

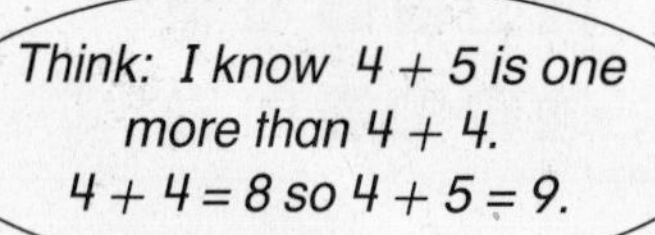

4 + 5 = 9

Find the sum. Use doubles to help.

1.

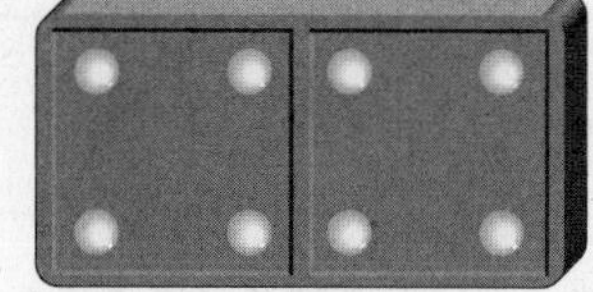

4 + 4 = 8

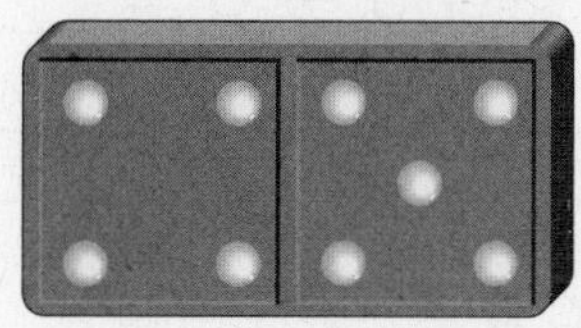

4 + 5 = ______

2.

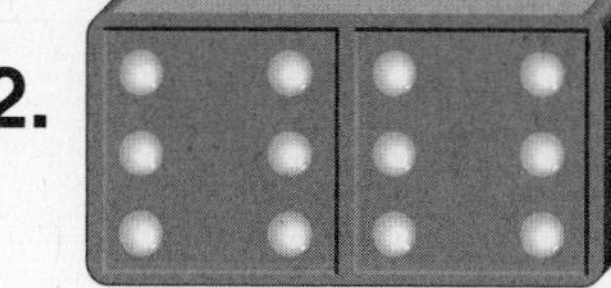

6 + 6 = ______

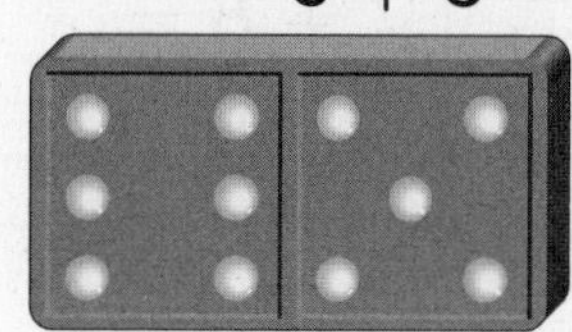

6 + 5 = ______

3. $\begin{array}{r} 5 \\ +5 \\ \hline \end{array}$ $\begin{array}{r} 5 \\ +6 \\ \hline \end{array}$

4. $\begin{array}{r} 8 \\ +8 \\ \hline \end{array}$ $\begin{array}{r} 8 \\ +9 \\ \hline \end{array}$

5. $\begin{array}{r} 6 \\ +6 \\ \hline \end{array}$ $\begin{array}{r} 6 \\ +7 \\ \hline \end{array}$

6. $\begin{array}{r} 8 \\ +8 \\ \hline \end{array}$ $\begin{array}{r} 8 \\ +7 \\ \hline \end{array}$

7. $\begin{array}{r} 10 \\ +10 \\ \hline \end{array}$ $\begin{array}{r} 10 \\ +9 \\ \hline \end{array}$

8. $\begin{array}{r} 7 \\ +7 \\ \hline \end{array}$ $\begin{array}{r} 7 \\ +8 \\ \hline \end{array}$

Name ____________________

2-5

Skills Practice

2NS2.1

Near Doubles

Find the sum. Use near doubles to help.

1.

$$\begin{array}{r} 6 \\ +\ 6 \\ \hline \end{array} \qquad \begin{array}{r} 7 \\ +\ 6 \\ \hline \end{array}$$

2.

$$\begin{array}{r} 9 \\ +\ 9 \\ \hline \end{array} \qquad \begin{array}{r} 9 \\ +\ 8 \\ \hline \end{array}$$

Find the sum. Use doubles and near doubles to help.

3.

7 + 7 = ____	
one less	*one more*
7 + 6 = ____	7 + 8 = ____

4.

5 + 5 = ____	
one less	*one more*
5 + 4 = ____	5 + 6 = ____

5.

6 + 6= ____	
one less	*one more*
6 + 5 = ____	6 + 7 = ____

6.

9 + 9 = ____	
one less	*one more*
9 + 8 = ____	9 + 10 = ____

7. Annie sees 4 bullfrogs at the lake. Zack sees one less bullfrog than Annie. Write an addition sentence that tells how many bullfrogs they saw.

____ + ____ = ____ bullfrogs

8. Marcy finds 5 ladybugs. Lee finds 1 more ladybug than Marcy. Write an addition sentence that tells how many ladybugs they found.

____ + ____ = ____ ladybugs

Name ______________________________

2-6

Reteach

2NS2.2

Make a 10

Chapter Resources

You can make a 10 to help you add.

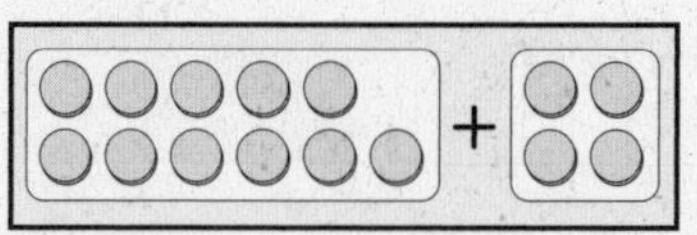

9 + 4

Move 1 to make a 10.

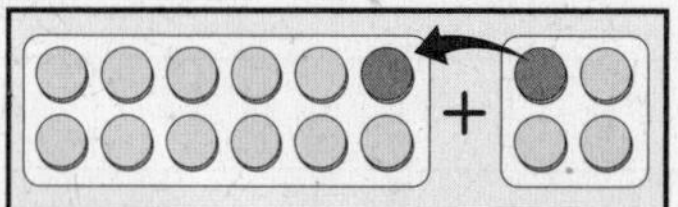

10 + 3

Now add 10 + 3.

10 + 3 = 13

9 + 4 = 13

Add. Color the counters you use to make a 10.

1. 7 + 6 can be changed to 10 + 3 = ____

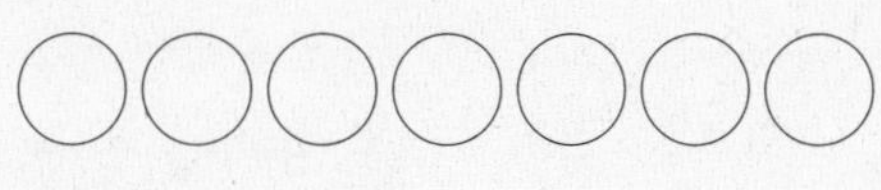

2. 8 + 3 can be changed to 10 + 1 = ____

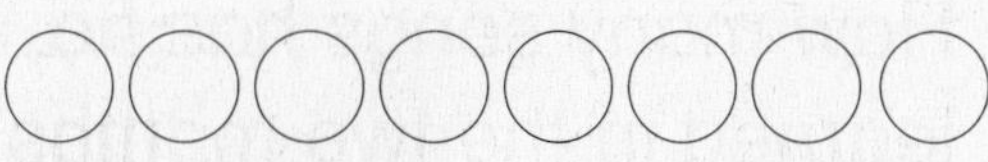

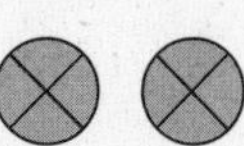

3. 6 + 9 = ____   ____ + 10 = ____

4. 8 + 6 = ____   10 + ____ = ____

Name ______

2-6

Skills Practice

2NS2.2

Make a 10

Add. Use connecting cubes to help.

1. 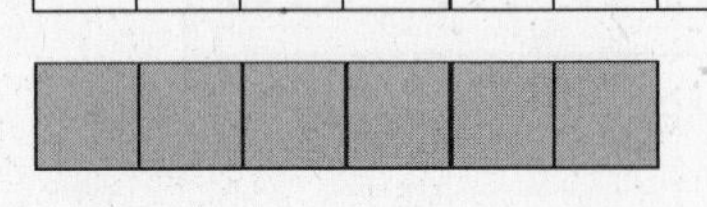

8 + 6 = 14 can be changed to 10 + 4 = 14

2. 7 + 7   8 + 6   9 + 4   9 + 5   8 + 4

3. 7 + 4 = ______   8 + 8 = ______   7 + 8 = ______

4. 9 + 7 = ______   6 + 7 = ______   8 + 9 = ______

Solve.

5. Ali built 8 model airplanes in October. In November she built 6 model airplanes.

How many airplanes has she built in all?

8 + ______ ______.

6. Marty learned to play 7 new songs in January. In February, he learned 5 new songs.

How many songs has he learned in the two months?

______ + ______ ______

Name ______________________________

2-7

Reteach

2AF1.1

Add Three Numbers

Chapter Resources

You can group addends. You can use doubles or make a 10.

Find a double.

4		
3		8
+ 4		+ 3
		11

Make a 10.

6		
5		10
+ 4		+ 5
		15

Find a double. Circle addends that make doubles. Add.

1.

3		4	4	4	5	3	7	5	
3	6	2	4	5		7		5	10
+ 7	+ 7	+ 2	___	+ 4	8	+ 3	6	+ 2	2
	13								

Make a 10. Circle addends that make a 10. Add.

2.

8		4	3	1		8	8	5	6
2	10	3	10	9	10	7	10	6	10
+ 4	+ 4	+ 6	___	+ 4	4	+ 3	___	+ 5	___
	14								

Find the sum.

3.

8		8		9		2		8	
3	3	9	8	9	18	7	7	0	0
+ 8	16	+ 1	10	+ 2	2	+ 8	10	+ 8	16

Name ______________________________

2-7

Skills Practice

2AF1.1

Add Three Numbers

Find each sum.

1.	3 2 + 3 8	4 5 + 4	8 0 + 2	4 3 + 4	5 4 + 6	9 1 + 5
2.	4 8 + 2	7 6 + 6	9 1 + 4	8 3 + 8	7 3 + 6	5 5 + 5
3.	4 6 + 8	3 5 + 3	0 7 + 7	2 4 + 8	8 2 + 3	3 6 + 7
4.	6 5 + 6	4 4 + 7	8 2 + 4	5 3 + 5	1 9 + 6	3 8 + 2

Solve.

5. Jan has 4 stamps. Tim has 9 stamps. Ben has 4 stamps. How many total stamps do they have?

______ stamps

6. There are 4 bear stickers, 6 wolf stickers, and 8 fox stickers. How many stickers are there in all?

______ stickers

Name ______

2-8

Reteach (1)

2MR1.1, 2AF1.1

Problem-Solving Investigation: Choose a Strategy

Chapter Resources

1. Jen: It takes me 10 minutes to clean my room.
It takes me 2 minutes to brush my teeth.
It takes me 5 minutes to change my clothes.
How long will it take me to get ready for bed?

Choose a strategy to solve.

Step 1
Understand

What do I know?

First step takes 10 minutes.

Next step takes 2 minutes.

Last step takes 5 minutes.

What do I need to find?

How much time in all will it take?

Step 2
Plan

How will I find how much time?

I can draw a picture.

Step 3
Solve

Draw a picture.

Step 1 room ~~||||~~ ~~||||~~
Step 2 teeth ~~||||~~
Step 3 change ||

Jen will take 17 minutes.

Step 4
Check

Did I draw a picture showing three parts? yes

Does my answer make sense? yes

Name ______________________________

2-8

Reteach (2)

2MR1.1, 2AF1.1

Problem-Solving Investigation: Choose a Strategy

Choose a strategy and solve.

Problem-Solving Strategies
Use logical reasoning
Act it out
Draw a picture

1. Candy, Dennis, and Serena are trading CDs. Candy gives 6 CDs to Serena and 5 CDs to Dennis. She has 6 CDs left over.

   How many CDs did she start with?

   ______ CDs

2. Keith has 4 drums. Shawn has the same number of drums.

   How many drums do they have in all?

   ______ drums

3. Nadia played 4 songs on the piano. Teresa played 2 songs on the banjo. Julio played 6 songs on the guitar.

   How many songs did they play?

   ______ songs

4. The band practices 6 hours a week. There was a 3-hour practice on Monday.

   How many hours are left to practice this week?

   ______ hours

Name ____________________

2-8

Skills Practice

2MR1.1, 2AF1.1

Problem-Solving Investigation: Choose a Strategy

Solve. Choose a strategy.

Problem-Solving Strategies
Draw a picture
Use logical reasoning
Act it out

1. Mrs. Adler washes 4 sweaters on Monday. On Tuesday, Mr. Adler washes one less sweater.

   How many sweaters have the Adlers washed in all?

   ______ sweaters

2. Ken has 2 blue shirts, 3 white shirts, and 7 striped shirts.

   How many total shirts does he have?

   ______ shirts

3. Linda is sewing beads onto her favorite hat. She uses 4 silver beads, 4 clear beads, and 6 gold beads.

   How many beads in all does Linda use?

   ______ beads

4. Together, Ike and Mike have 10 pairs of shoes.

   How many shoes are there in all?

   ______ shoes

5. Ivan is cleaning out a closet. He finds 4 hats. His sister finds one more hat than Ivan found.

   How many hats did they find altogether?

   ______ hats

Name ______

3-1

Reteach

2NS2.2

Count Back to Subtract

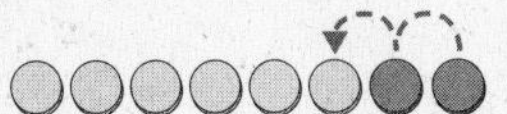

Count back to subtract.

8 − 2 = 6

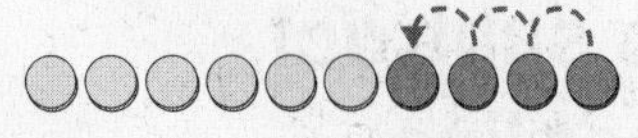

Count back to subtract.

10 − 4 = 6

Count back to subtract. Show how you use ◯ to help.

1. 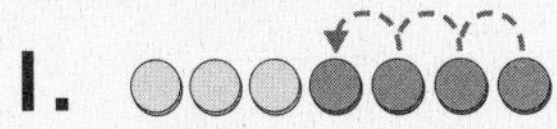

7 − 4 = 3

2. 9 − 0 = 9

3. 9 − 9 = 0

4. 5 − 1 = ______

5. 6 − 2 = ______

6. 9 − 4 = ______

7. 8 − 6 = ______

8. 4 − 3 = ______

9. 7 − 3 = ______

Name ______________________________

3-1

Skills Practice

2NS2.2

Count Back to Subtract

Count back to subtract.
Use the number line.

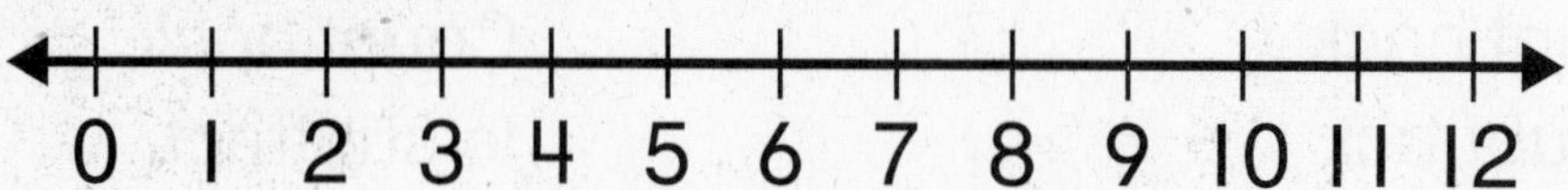

1. 12 – 4 = ______ 11 – 3 = ______ 7 – 1 = ______

2. 8 – 3 = ______ 6 – 2 = ______ 10 – 2 = ______

3. 9 – 1 = ______ 7 – 3 = ______ 12 – 3 = ______

4. 8 – 1 = ______ 11 – 2 = ______ 8 – 2 = ______

5. ______ = 10 – 1 ______ = 7 – 2 ______ = 10 – 3

Solve.

6. There are 9 dogs playing at the dog park.
3 dogs go home.

How many dogs are left?

______ dogs

7. There are 11 lions and 2 tigers at the zoo.

How many more lions than tigers are at the zoo?

______ lions

Name ______________________

3-2

Reteach

2NS2.2, 2MR1.2

Subtract All and Subtract Zero

5 – 0 = 5

Subtract **0**.
You have the same number left.

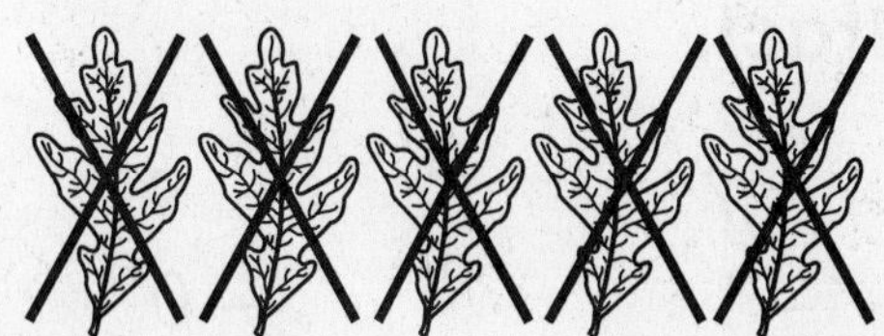

5 – 5 = 0

Subtract **all**.
You have 0 left.

Subtract. You can cross out pictures to help.

1.

9 – 0 = 9

9 – 9 = 0

2.

6 – 0 = ______

6 – 6 = ______

3.

4 – 0 = ______

4 – 4 = ______

4.

7 – 0 = ______

7 – 7 = ______

5.

8 – 0 = ______

8 – 8 = ______

6.

5 – 0 = ______

5 – 5 = ______

3-2

Name ______________________________

Skills Practice

2NS2.2, 2MR1.2

Subtract All and Subtract Zero

Subtract.

1.

7	9	8	10
− 1	− 0	− 8	− 2

2.

6	9	6	8
− 6	− 3	− 0	− 1

3.

9	7	9	10
− 1	− 7	− 2	− 1

4.

8	9	7	8
− 3	− 9	− 2	− 0

Solve.

5. 10 children play ball. After they finish, all 10 go back to class.

How many children keep playing ball?

______ children

6. 8 girls take a walk. When they reach the park, they all keep walking.

How many girls are still taking a walk?

______ girls

Name ______________________________

3-3

Reteach

2NS2.2, 2MR1.2

Use Doubles to Subtract

You can use doubles facts to subtract.

Remember, doubles are addends that are the same number.

If you know 6 + 6 = 12, you know 12 − 6 = 6

Subtract. Use doubles facts to help.

1.

4 + 4 = 8, so

8 − 4 = ______

2.

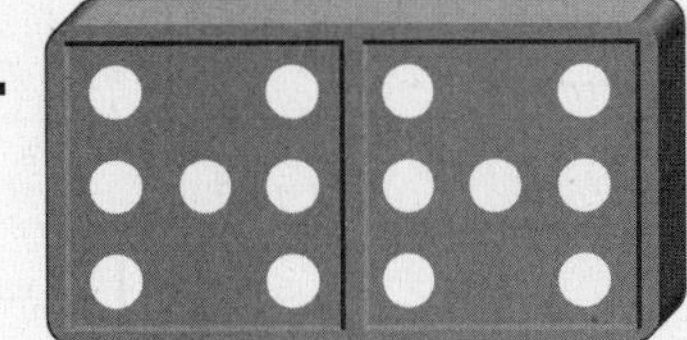

7 + 7 = ______, so

14 − 7 = ______

3.

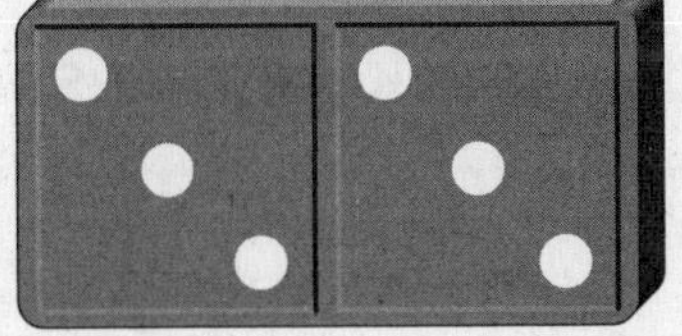

3 + 3 = ______, so

6 − 3 = ______

4.

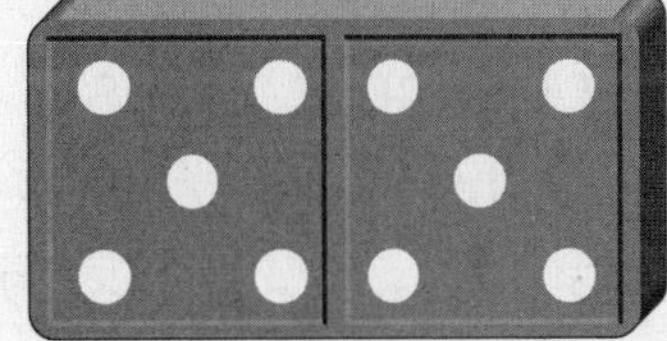

5 + 5 = ______, so

10 − 5 = ______

5. 8 + 8 = ______, so

16 − 8 = ______

6. 9 + 9 = ______, so

18 − 9 = ______

3-3

Name ______________________________

Skills Practice

2NS2.2, 2MR1.2

Use Doubles to Subtract

Subtract. Circle any problems in which you can use doubles to subtract.

1. 7 − 7 = ____ 12 − 6 = ____ 4 − 0 = ____ 8 − 3 = ____ 11 − 3 = ____

2. 10 − 5 = ____ 4 − 2 = ____ 8 − 4 = ____ 8 − 0 = ____ 7 − 7 = ____

3. 7 − 3 = ______ 18 − 9 = ______ 7 − 7 = ______

4. 16 − 8 = ______ 10 − 3 = ______ 14 − 7 = ______

Solve.

5. Shaun buys 10 erasers. He gives 5 erasers to Fred.

How many erasers does Shaun have left? What doubles fact can help you?

______ + ______ = ______

Write a number sentence to find how many erasers Shaun has left.

______ − ______ = ______

______ erasers are left

6. Sylvia has 6 markers. She gives 3 markers to Clarice.

How many markers does Sylvia have left? What doubles fact can help you?

______ + ______ = ______

Write a number sentence that tells how many markers are left.

______ − ______ = ______

______ markers are left

Name ______________________________

3-4

Reteach (1)

2SDAP2.1, 2MR1.0

Problem-Solving Strategy: Find a Pattern

Chapter Resources

There are 5 dogs. How many legs are there in all?

Step 1
Understand

Be sure you understand the problem.

What do you know?

- There are __4__ legs on a dog.
- There are __5__ dogs.

What do you need to find out?

- I need to find __how many legs in all.__

Step 2
Plan

- Draw a Picture
- Make a Table
- Guess and Check
- Find a Pattern
- Make a List

Make a plan.

Choose a strategy from the list.

If you know how many legs one dog has, you can use a pattern to figure out how many legs 2 dogs have. Then, you can keep the pattern going.

Step 3
Solve

Carry out your plan. Make a chart.

Number of dogs	1	2	3	4	5
Number of legs	4				

There are ______ legs in all.

Step 4
Check

Look back.

Does my answer make sense? Yes No

Name ____________________

3-4

Reteach (2)

2SDAP2.1, 2MR1.0

Problem-Solving Strategy: Find a Pattern

Solve.

1. Sam and Andy are stacking blocks. They add blocks 4 at a time. If it does not fall, how high will the stack be after each boy takes 3 turns?

	Sam			Andy		
Turn	1	2	3	4	5	6
Blocks	4	8	12	16		

The stack will be ______ blocks high.

2. Andy works on his spelling. These are his scores for the last 5 tests. If this pattern continues for 8 tests, what will Andy's highest score be?

Test	1	2	3	4	5	6	7	8
Score	30	33	36	39	42			

Antonio's highest score will be ______.

3. Rachel's school bus takes 14 children home. Two children get off at each stop. If this pattern continues, how many stops will it take until there are no more children on the bus?

Stop	School	1	2	3				
Children still on bus	14	12	10	8				

There are no more children on the bus after ______ stops.

Name ______________________________

3-4

Skills Practice

2SDAP2.1, 2MR1.0

Problem-Solving Strategy: Find a Pattern

Find a pattern to solve.

1. One week Max rides his bike 2 miles. Week two he rides 6 miles. Week three he rides 10 miles. In week four, he rides 14 miles. If this pattern continues, how many miles does he ride during week 7?

week	1	2	3	4	5	6	7
miles	2	6	10	14			

Max rides ______ miles.

---

2. A coach orders shirts for the team. The numbers on the first four shirts are 02, 04, 06, and 08. If the pattern stays the same, what will be the numbers on the next three shirts?

shirt	1	2	3	4	5	6	7
number	02	04	06	08			

The shirts have numbers ______, ______, and ______.

---

3. Nell writes numbers on cards and asks her sister to help her with the pattern. So far, the numbers on the cards are 17, 15, 13, 11. If the pattern stays the same, what will the next three cards be?

cards	17	15	13	11			

The next three cards will be ______, ______, and ______.

Name ______________________________

3-5

Reteach

2NS2.1, 2MR3.0

Relate Addition to Subtraction

8 + 4 = 12

12 − 4 = 8

These addition and subtraction facts have the same three numbers.

Use addition facts to subtract.

1.

4 + 7 = 11

11 − 7 = 4

2. 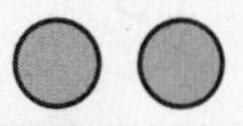 

3 + 6 = ______

9 − 3 = ______

---

3.  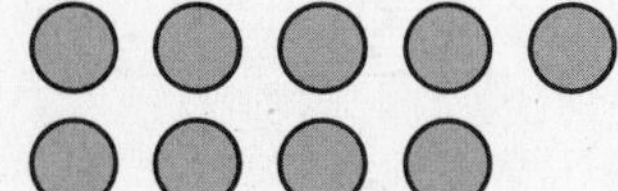  

9 + 3 = ______

12 − 3 = ______

4.   

2 + 5 = ______

7 − 5 = ______

---

5. 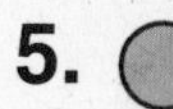  

2 + 8 = ______

10 − 2 = ______

6.   

1 + 6 = ______

7 − 6 = ______

Name ______________________________

3-5

Skills Practice

2NS2.1, 2MR3.0

Relate Addition to Subtraction

Use addition facts to subtract.

1. $8 + 5 =$ 13 | $6 + 8 =$ ____ | $6 + 7 =$ ____

$13 - 5 =$ ____ | $14 - 8 =$ ____ | $13 - 7 =$ ____

2. $4 + 9 =$ ____ | $8 + 8 =$ ____ | $6 + 9 =$ ____

$13 - 4 =$ ____ | $16 - 8 =$ ____ | $15 - 6 =$ ____

3. $3 + 8$ | $11 - 8$ | $4 + 8$ | $12 - 8$ | $7 + 7$ | $14 - 7$

4. $8 + 7$ | $15 - 8$ | $9 + 7$ | $16 - 9$ | $8 + 9$ | $17 - 8$

5. $5 + 9$ | $14 - 5$ | $3 + 9$ | $12 - 3$ | $9 + 9$ | $18 - 9$

Solve.

6. There are 16 stamps. Pete uses 8 of the stamps. How many stamps are left?

____ stamps

7. Megan writes 4 letters on Monday. She writes 9 letters on Tuesday. How many letters does Megan write?

____ letters

3-6

Name ______________________________

Reteach

2NS2.1

Missing Addends

9 + ☐ = 14

Related facts use the same three numbers.

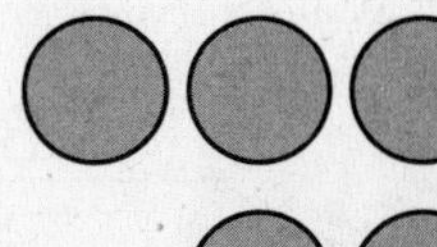

Write a related fact.

14 − 9 = ___5___,

so, 9 + ___5___ = 14.

Find the missing addend. Draw pictures to help.

1. 8 + [4] = 12

12 − 8 = [4]

2. 7 + ☐ = 12

12 − 7 = ☐

3. 5 + ☐ = 13

13 − 5 = ☐

4. 9 + ☐ = 17

17 − 9 = ☐

5. 8 + ☐ = 14

14 − ☐ = 8

Name ______________________________

3-6 Skills Practice

2NS2.1

Missing Addends

Find each missing addend.

1. 3 + [9] = 12   14 − 7 = □   □ + 8 = 14

2.

4	12	6	14	7	15
+ 7	− □	+ 9	− 8	+ 7	− 7
□	4	□	□	□	□

3.

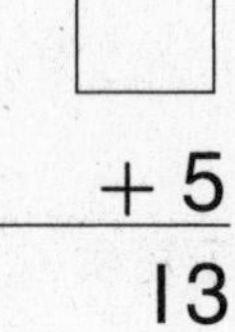

□	16	6	17	□	14
+ 5	− □	+ 7	− □	+ 9	− □
13	8	□	8	14	9

4.

7	11	□	18	□	15
+ □	− □	+ 8	− 9	+ 4	− □
10	5	13	□	11	8

5.

□	10	6	16	8	16
+ 4	− □	+ 6	− □	+ □	− 9
12	4	□	7	17	□

Solve.

6. Jeff has 9 stamps. He gets 3 more. How many stamps does he have now?

_____ stamps

7. Gina has 15 postcards. 7 are from the United States. How many are not from the United States?

_____ postcards

Name ______________________

3-7

Reteach

2NS2.1, 2MR3.0

Fact Families

Some fact families have two addition facts and two subtraction facts.

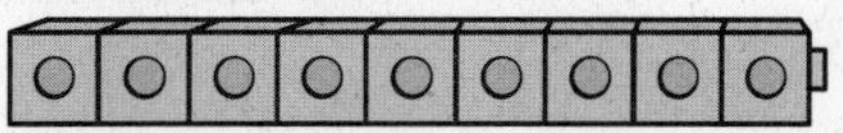

9 + 7 = 16   16 − 7 = 9

7 + 9 = 16   16 − 9 = 7

Some fact families have one addition fact and one subtraction fact.

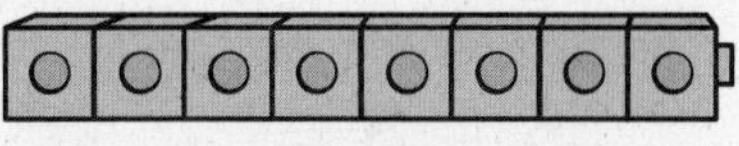

8 + 8 = 16   16 − 8 = 8

Complete each fact family.

1. 9 + 4 = 13   13 − 9 = 4

   4 + 9 = 13   13 − 4 = 9

---

2. 6 + 5 = ____   11 − 5 = ____

   5 + 6 = ____   11 − 6 = ____

---

3. 9 + 8 = ____   17 − 9 = ____

   8 + 9 = ____   17 − 8 = ____

---

4. 7 + 7 = ____   14 − 7 = ____

Name ____________________

3-7

Skills Practice

2NS2.1, 2MR3.0

Fact Families

Complete each fact family.

1. 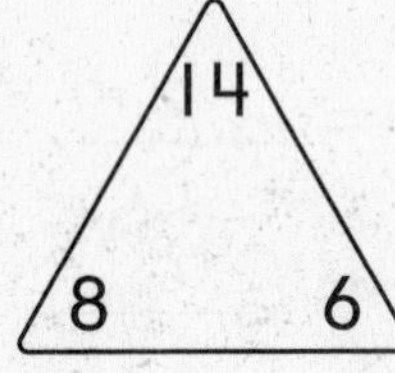

$8 + 6 =$ 14

$6 + 8 =$ ______

$14 - 8 =$ ______

$14 - 6 =$ ______

2. 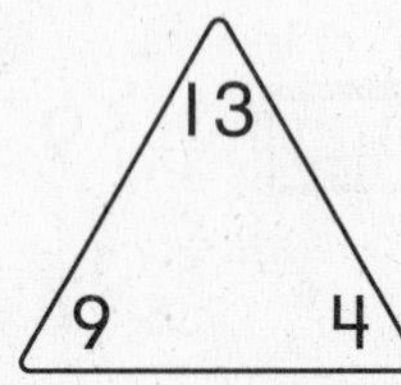

$9 + 4 =$ ______

$4 + 9 =$ ______

$13 - 9 =$ ______

$13 - 4 =$ ______

3. 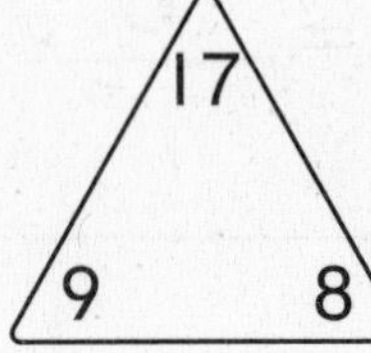

$8 + 9 =$ ______

$9 + 8 =$ ______

$17 - 8 =$ ______

$17 - 9 =$ ______

4. 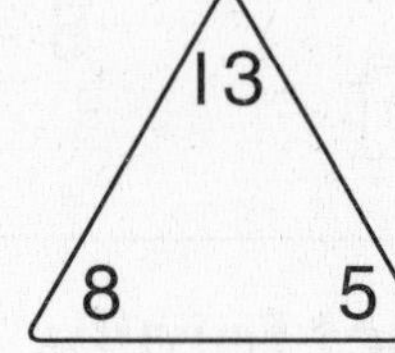

$5 + 8 =$ ______

$8 + 5 =$ ______

$13 - 5 =$ ______

$13 - 8 =$ ______

5. 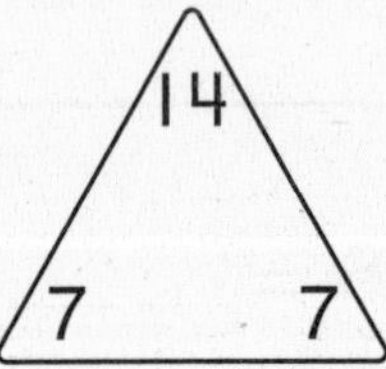

______ $+ 7 = 14$

$14 - 7 =$ ______

6. 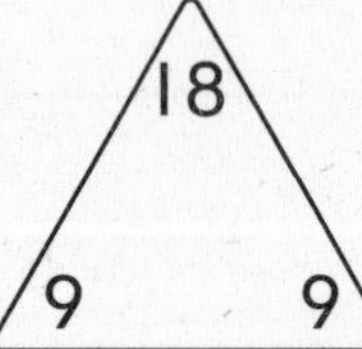

______ $+ 9 = 18$

$18 -$ ______ $= 9$

Solve. Write the number sentences in the fact family.

7. Lucas has 7 toy cars and 8 toy trucks. He has 15 toys in all. Write the number sentences in the fact family.

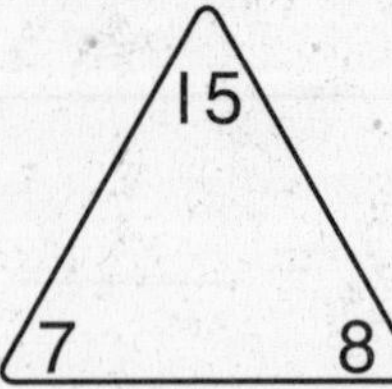

____ + ____ = ____

____ + ____ = ____

____ − ____ = ____

____ − ____ = ____

Name ____________________

3-8

Reteach (1)

2AF1.2, 2MR1.1

Problem-Solving Investigation: Choose a Strategy

Chapter Resources

1. Kim's mom makes 13 blueberry pancakes. Kim eats some. There are 9 pancakes left when she finishes. How many pancakes did Kim eat?

Choose a problem-solving strategy to solve.

Step 1 **Understand**	**What do you know?** Mom makes 13 pancakes. 9 pancakes are left. **What do I need to find?** How many pancakes Kim ate.
Step 2 **Plan**	**How will I find how many Kim ate?** I can write a number sentence.
Step 3 **Solve**	13 – 9 = ______ Kim ate ______ pancakes.
Step 4 **Check**	Did I write a number sentence? yes Does my answer make sense? yes

Name ____________________

3-8

Reteach (2)

2AF1.2, 2MR1.1

Problem-Solving Investigation: Choose a Strategy

Problem-Solving Strategies
Find a Pattern
Logical Reasoning
Write a Number Sentence

Solve. | **Show your work here.**

1. Kyra has 17 stickers. She loses 9 stickers. How many stickers does she have left?

   Krya has ______ stickers.

2. Julia makes a pattern with stars.

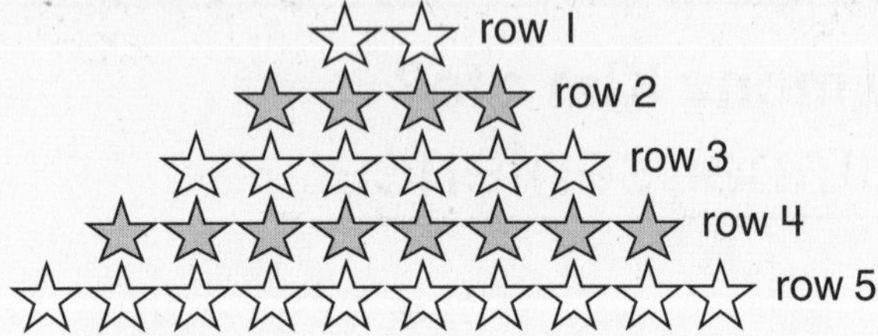

   If the pattern continues, how many stars will be in row 8?

   ______ stars

3. Eldon had 15 fish. He gave some to his brother. Now Eldon has 6 fish.

   How many fish did Eldon give to his brother?

   ______ fish

Name ______________________________

3-8

Skills Practice

2AF1.2, 2MR1.1

Problem-Solving Investigation: Choose a Strategy

Problem-Solving Strategies
Find a Pattern
Logical Reasoning
Write a Number Sentence

Solve.

Show your work here.

1. At the toy store there are 3 toys on the top shelf. 6 toys are on shelf two. 9 toys are on shelf 3. If the pattern continues, how many toys will be on shelf 6?

______ toys.

2. There are 20 toys in the store window. Five toys are trains. Four toys are dolls. Six toys are airplanes. The rest of the toys are games. How many toys are games?

______ games

3. Three children are in line to pay for toys. Anna is not second. Ben is in line after Juan. Juan is not first. In what order will the children pay for their toys?

______; ______; ______

4-1

Name ____________________

Reteach

2SDAP1.1, 2SDAP1.4

Take a Survey

Use the survey to answer each question.

Look at your classmates. Make one tally mark to record what each classmate is wearing. Complete the chart.

Clothes in the Classroom	
Jeans	
Sweaters	
T-Shirts	
Skirts	

1. How many students are wearing sweaters?

   ____

2. How many students are wearing t-shirts?

   ____

3. Which got more tallies, jeans or skirts?

   ____

4. What item of clothing is worn the least?

   ____

5. What item of clothing is worn the most?

   ____

4-1

Name ______________________

Skills Practice

2SDAP1.1, 2SDAP1.4

Take a Survey

Use the survey to answer each question.

Ask classmates which hobby they like best. Use tally marks to record their answers. Complete the chart.

Favorite Hobby	
Sports	
Building Models	
Painting	
Playing Music	

1. How many tally marks did playing music get?

   ____

2. Which hobby has the most tally marks?

   ____

3. Wes is starting a Craft Club. He wants to invite the students who like building models or painting. Write a number sentence to show how many students Wes should invite.

   ____ + ____ = ____

4. Sue wants to add cooking to the chart. Three students decide to change their vote from playing music to cooking. How many tallies are left for playing music?

   ____

Name ____________________

4-2

Reteach

2SDAP1.2, 2SDAP1.4

Picture Graphs

The picture graph shows the votes for favorite sport.

Favorite Sport	
Baseball	
Basketball	
Soccer	

Use the picture graph. Fill in the pictograph below.

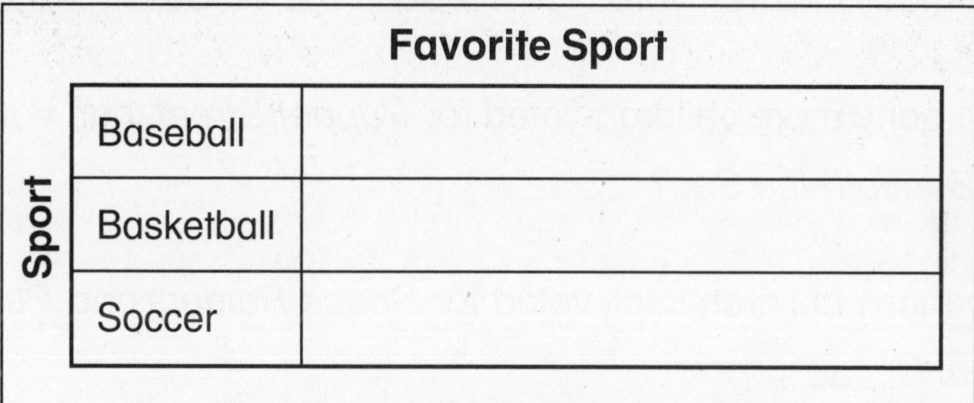

Favorite Sport

Sport	
Baseball	
Basketball	
Soccer	

Key: Each ☺ stands for 2 votes.

1. How many more students voted for baseball than for basketball?

   ______ more students

2. Which sport is the favorite? __________

3. How many students voted in all? ______

Name ____

4-2

Skills Practice

2SDAP1.2, 2SDAP1.4

Pictographs

Some students voted for their favorite book. Show their tally chart as a pictograph. Use the graph to answer each question.

Favorite Book	
Space Raiders	𝍸 𝍸
Beneath the Sea	𝍸 |||
House in the Woods	𝍸 𝍸 ||
Puppet Street	𝍸 𝍸

Favorite Book

Space Raiders							
Beneath the Sea							
House in the Woods							
Puppet Street							

Key: Each stands for 2 votes.

1. How many children voted for *House in the Woods*? ______

2. How many more children voted for *Puppet Street* than voted for *Beneath the Sea*? ______

3. How many children in all voted for *Space Raiders* and *Puppet Street*? ______

4. Lila wants to read the book with the least votes. Which book should she read? ____________________

5. Rick, Tom, and Cindy like *Space Raiders* the best. If their votes are added to the survey, will *Space Raiders* have the most votes? ______

Name ______________________________

4-3

Reteach (1)

2MR2.2, 2AF1.3

Problem-Solving Strategy: Write a Number Sentence

Chapter Resources

How many stuffed animals does Ella have?

Ella's Toy Collection

Stuffed Bears	🧸	🧸	🧸	🧸	🧸				
Stuffed Mice	🐭	🐭	🐭	🐭	🐭	🐭	🐭	🐭	
Dolls	🙂	🙂	🙂						

Step 1
Understand

What do I know?

Bears are stuffed.
Mice are stuffed.

What do I need to find?

How many bears and mice together?

Step 2
Plan

What can I do?

I will write a number sentence to add the bears and mice.

Step 3
Solve

Write a number sentence.

______ bears + ______ mice = ______ stuffed animals

Step 4
Check

Are there 13 stuffed animals shown in the chart?

______

Name ______________________________

4-3

Reteach (2)

2MR2.2, 2AF1.3

Problem-Solving Strategy: Write a Number Sentence

Use the graphs to answer the questions. Write a number sentence to solve.

Ms. Garcia's Shopping List	
Tomatoes	𝍸 |||
Potatoes	𝍸 |
Chickens	|||

1. How many vegetables will Ms. Garcia buy?

______ tomatoes ______ potatoes = ______ vegetables.

Nate's World Stamp Collection

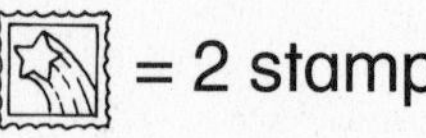 = 2 stamps

Italy	▣	▣	▣	▣	▣					
Japan	▣	▣	▣	▣	▣	▣	▣	▣	▣	▣
Mexico	▣	▣	▣	▣	▣	▣	▣	▣		

2. How many more of Nate's stamps are from Japan than are from Mexico? ______ from Japan ______ from Mexico = ______

3. How many stamps are from either Italy or Mexico? ______ from Italy ______ from Mexico = ______

Name ___________________________________

4-3

Skills Practice

2MR2.2, 2AF1.3

Problem-Solving Strategy: Write a Number Sentence

Use the graph. Write a number sentence to solve.

Number of Animals at Paolo's Pets

Parrots	🦜	🦜	🦜	🦜	🦜	🦜	🦜	🦜		
Snakes	🐍	🐍	🐍	🐍	🐍					
Lizards	🦎	🦎	🦎	🦎	🦎	🦎	🦎	🦎	🦎	🦎

1. How many more lizards than snakes?

_____ − _____ = _____

2. Pablo takes a photo of each parrot and each snake. How many photos does Pablo take?

_____ + _____ = _____ photos

Evans Family Recycling

Paper	♻	♻	♻	♻						
Plastic	♻	♻	♻	♻	♻	♻				
Glass	♻	♻	♻							

Key: Each ♻ stands for 2 items.

3. How many more paper items than glass items?

_____ − _____ = _____

4. The Evans family can put plastic and glass items in the same bin. How many items are in this bin?

_____ + _____ = _____ items

5. Jim knows his family recycles twice as much paper as the Evans family does. How many paper items does Jim's family recycle?

_____ + _____ = _____ paper items

4-4

Name ______________________

Reteach

2SDAP1.1, 2SDAP1.4

Bar Graphs

Preparation: Crayons are needed for this activity.

Bar graphs use bars to show data. You can make a bar graph with data you read. Read the data to complete the bar graph.

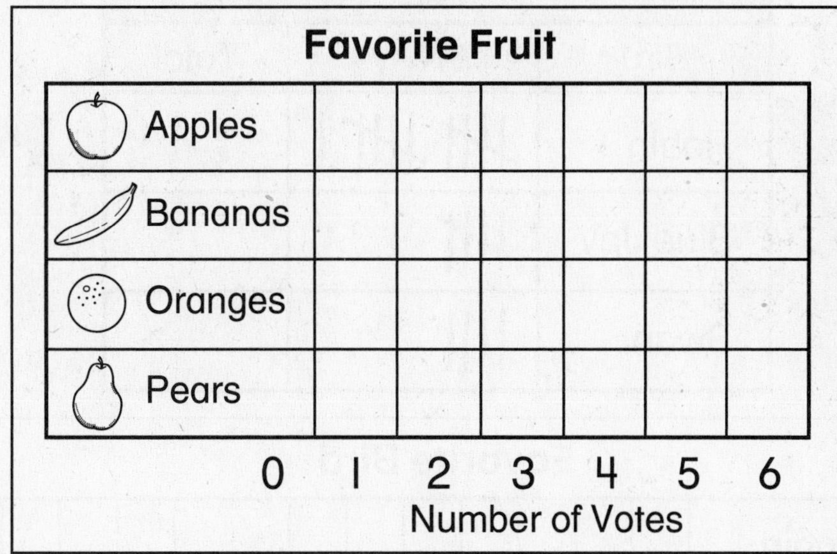

Data:

Four people voted for apples. Show this on the bar graph.

Five people voted for oranges. Show this on the bar graph.

Two people voted for pears. Show this on the bar graph.

Three people voted for bananas. Show this on the bar graph.

Answer each question.

1. What is the title of this bar graph? ______________________

2. How many kinds of fruit are shown in the bar graph? ______

3. How many votes did apples get? ______

4. What is the favorite fruit? ____________

4-4

Name ____________________

Skills Practice

2SDAP1.1, 2SDAP1.4

Bar Graphs

Preparation: Crayons are needed for this activity.

Use data from the chart to make a bar graph. Color one space for each vote. Then answer each question.

Favorite Bird		
Bird	Tally	Total
Robin	𝍸 𝍸 |	11
Blue Jay	𝍸	
Swan	||||	

Favorite Bird

Robin												
Blue Jay												
Swan												
	1	2	3	4	5	6	7	8	9	10	11	12

Number of Votes

1. Which bird got the most votes? ____________

2. How many more students voted for the *robin* than the *swan*?

______

3. How many votes for blue jays does the graph show? ______

4. How many students voted in all? ______

Name ______________________________

4-5

Reteach

2SDAP1.2, 2AF1.3

Different Ways to Show Data

You can show the same data different ways. You can use the data on one graph to make more graphs. Count how many tallies to help.

Favorite Meal		
Breakfast	𝍸	
Lunch	𝍸 III	
Dinner	III	

1. Use the data from the tally chart to make the picture graph.

Favorite Meal

Breakfast	
Lunch	
Dinner	

Key: Each ☺ stands for 1 vote.

2. Use the data from the picture graph to color the bar graph.

Favorite Meal

Meal								
Breakfast								
Lunch								
Dinner								
	0	1	2	3	4	5	6	7	8

Number of Votes

4-5

Name ______________________________

Skills Practice

2SDAP1.2, 2AF1.3

Different Ways to Show Data

Preparation: Crayons are needed for this activity.

Use the tally chart. Make a pictograph and a bar graph to show the data. Then answer the questions.

Our Favorite Dinner		
Food	Tally	Total
Spaghetti	𝍸 I	6
Soup	IIII	
Taco	𝍸 III	

Our Favorite Dinner

Dinner								
Spaghetti								
Soup								
Taco								
	0	1	2	3	4	5	6	7	8

Number of Votes

Our Favorite Dinner	
Spaghetti	
Soup	
Taco	

Key: Each 🯅 stands for 2 votes.

1. Which dinner got the most votes? ________

2. Which dinner got the fewest votes? ________

3. How many students voted? ______

4. How many more students chose tacos than soup? ______

5. Kim lists the dinners from least favorite to most favorite. What dinner is second on her list? ____________

Name ______________________________

4-6 Reteach

2SDAP1.3, 2SDAP1.4

Range and Mode

Range and mode are ways to talk about data. Data is information. Looking at data in a simple way can help you find the range and mode.

Mrs. Lee's class did a survey about TVs in the home.

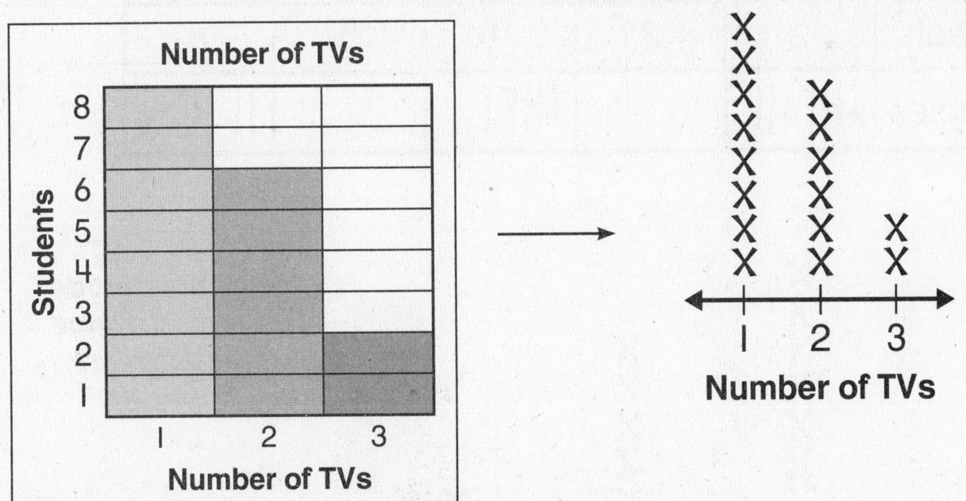

Use the graphs to find mode and range.

Remember:
mode = most.

1. On both graphs, circle the number of TVs you see most often.

This number is the **mode**. _____ is the **mode**.

2. Look at the graph. Write the greatest number TVs a family has: _____.

Write the least number of TVs a family has: _____

The **range** is the difference between these numbers. Write a number sentence to find the **range**: _____ − _____ = _____

The **range** is _____.

Name ____

4-6

Skills Practice

2SDAP1.3, 2SDAP1.4

Range and Mode

Norah has recorded how many people can sit at each table in her cafe. The data shows how many of each table she has. Find the mode. Find the range.

Norah's Cafe Seating					
Number of Seats	2	3	4	5	6
Number of Tables	𝍸 |||		𝍸		||

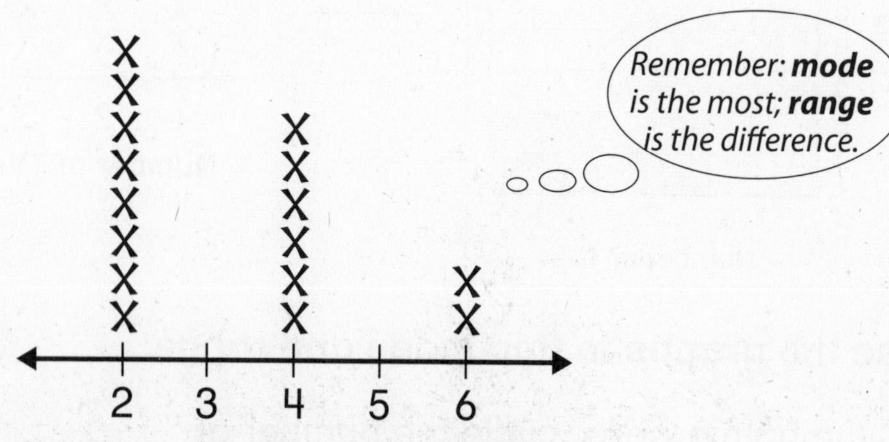

Number of Seats at Each Table

Use the graph to solve.

1. Put the data in order from *least* to *greatest*.
2 ____

2. Circle the **mode** on the graph. Write the mode. ______

3. Find the **range**. Write a number sentence to solve.
______ − ______ = ______

Name

4-7

Reteach (1)

2MR1.1, 2NS3.1

Problem-Solving Investigation: Choose a Strategy

Chapter Resources

Aaron has 3 muffin pans. Each pan can hold 6 muffins. How many muffins can Aaron bake?

Understand

What do I know?

Aaron has 3 pans. Each pan holds 6 muffins.

What do I need to find out?

How many muffins can Aaron bake?

Plan

How will I find how many?

I can make a table. A table can show both drawings and numbers clearly.

Solve

Number of Pans	Number of Muffins
1	6
2	12
3	18

Aaron can bake ______ muffins.

Check

Look back.

Did I use the table to find out how many? yes

4-7

Name ______________________________

Reteach (2)

2MR1.1, 2AF1.2

Problem-Solving Investigation: Choose a Strategy

Solve.

Problem-Solving Strategies
Draw a Picture
Find a Pattern
Make a Table

Show your work here.

1. Jake is making up a new dance. He hops, hops, turns, hops, hops, and turns. What do you think he will do next?

______

2. 3 turtles can fit in 1 tank. Jose has 3 tanks. How many turtles can he have?

______ turtles

3. Joy brings 7 treats for the class. Jessie brings 14 treats. How many more treats did Jessie bring than Joy?

______

4. Jin, Jack, and Julia want to feed the birds. They each bring 2 bags of seed. How many bags of seed are there in all?

______ bags of seed

Name ______________________________

4-7

Skills Practice

2MR1.1, 2AF1.2

Problem-Solving Investigation: Choose a Strategy

Chapter Resources

Solve.

Problem-Solving Strategies
Draw a Picture
Find a Pattern
Make a Table

Show your work here.

1. Shandra is giving a treat bag to each of her 3 friends. She puts 4 pear slices in each bag. How many pear slices are there in all?

______ pear slices

2. Liam is writing the number of eggs his hens have. 1 hen has 2 eggs. 2 hens have 4 eggs. 3 hens have 6 eggs. Liam guesses that 4 hens will have 8 eggs. Is this a good guess?

______

3. Kiki, Greg, and Seth are making snowmen. Each snowman needs 1 carrot for a nose. Kiki brings 4 carrots. Greg brings 2 carrots. Seth brings 5 carrots. Are there enough carrots to make 12 snowmen?______

How many snowmen can they make? ______

Name ___________________________

5-1

Reteach

2NS2.3

Add Tens

Chapter Resources

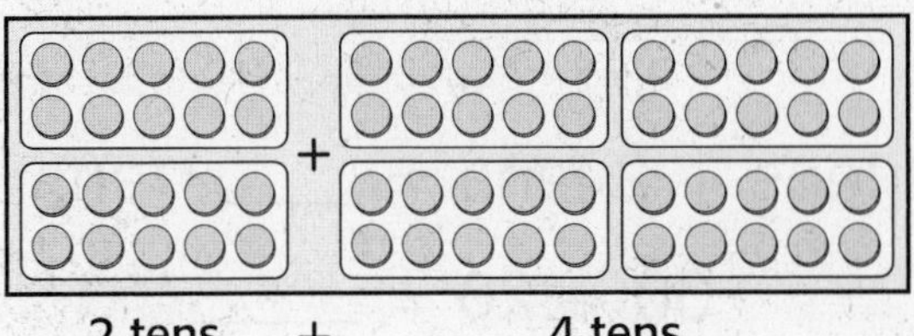

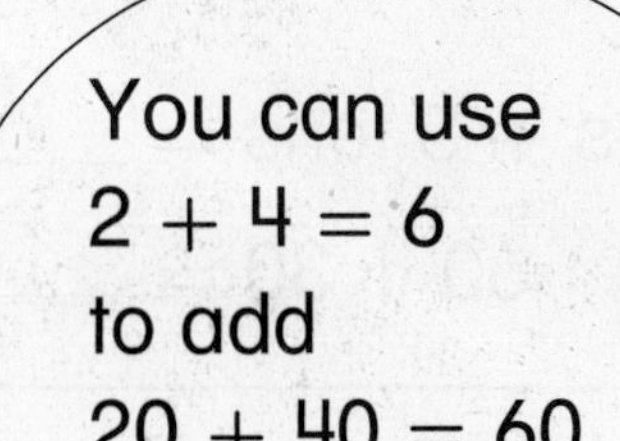

2 tens + 4 tens = 6 tens

20 + 40 = 60

Add. Use the addition facts and counters to help.

1.

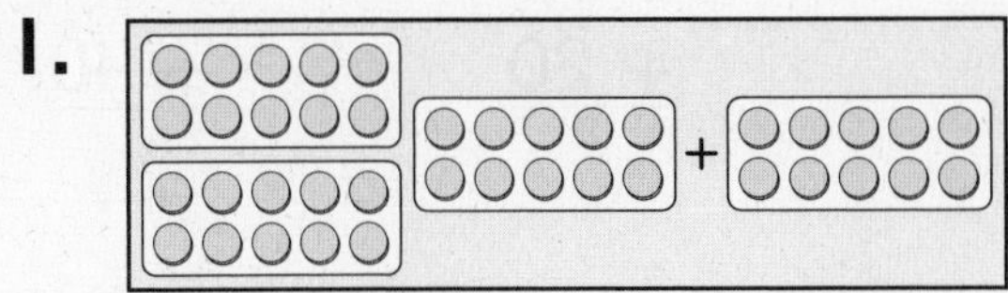

3 tens + 1 ten = _____ tens

30 + 10 = _____

2.

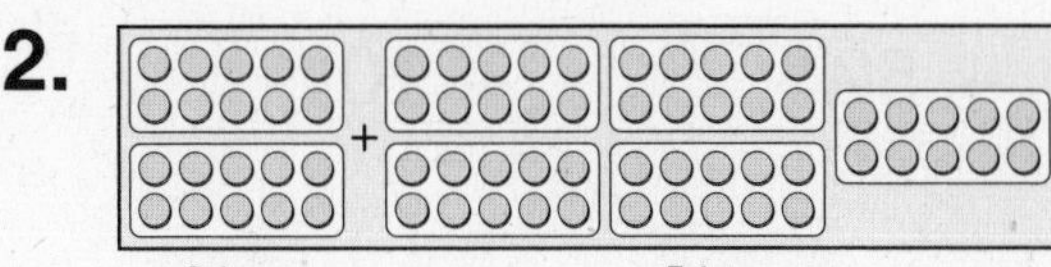

2 tens + 5 tens = _____ tens

20 + 50 = _____

3.

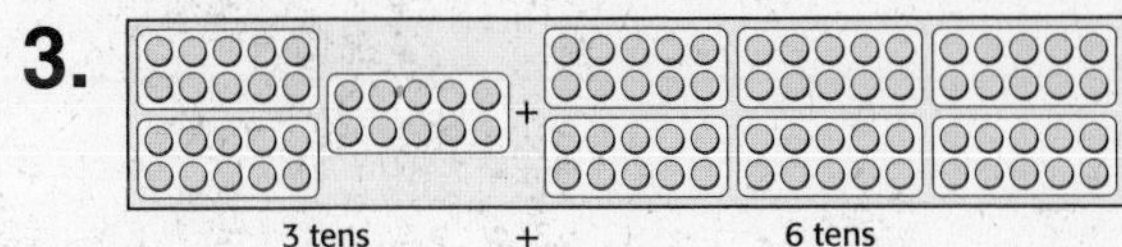

3 tens + 6 tens = _____ tens

30 + 60 = _____

4.

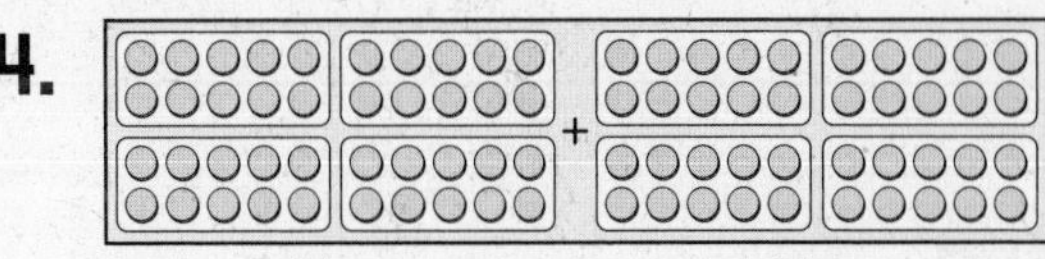

4 tens + 4 tens = _____ tens

40 + 40 = _____

5.

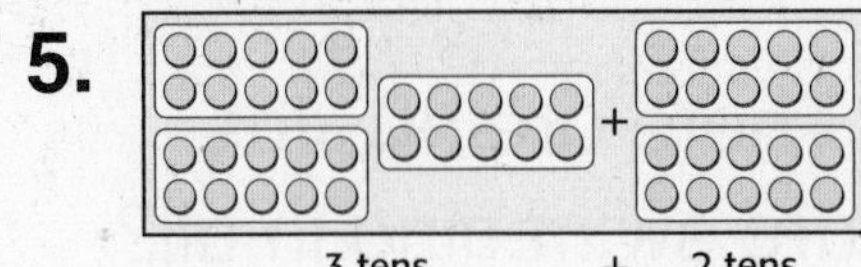

3 tens + 2 tens = _____ tens

30 + 20 = _____

6.

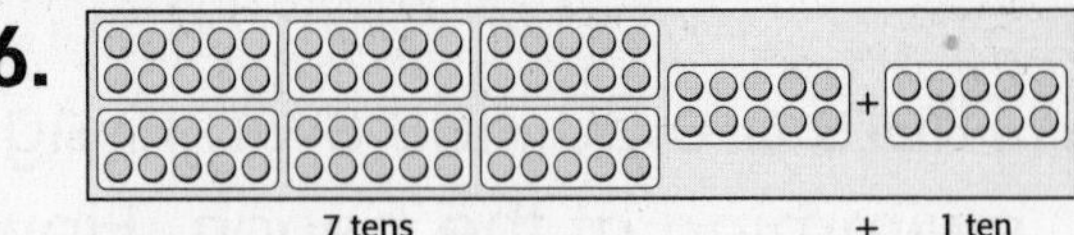

7 tens + 1 ten = _____ tens

70 + 10 = _____

Name ____________________

5-1

Skills Practice

2NS2.3

Add Tens

Add.

1. 6 tens + 3 tens = __9__ tens 3 tens + 2 tens = _____ tens

60 + 30 = _____ 30 + 20 = _____

2.

30	50	20	10	60
+ 40	+ 20	+ 30	+ 70	+ 10

3.

30	40	20	70	40
+ 50	+ 20	+ 60	+ 20	+ 40

4.

50	10	30	40	80
+ 10	+ 20	+ 30	+ 50	+ 10

Solve.

5. Bob sees 10 trees near his school. He sees 20 trees at the park. How many trees does he see in all?

_____ trees

6. There are 30 kids swimming at the pool. There are 40 kids swimming at the beach. How many kids are swimming in all?

_____ kids

5-2

Name ______

Reteach

2AF1.2

Count On Tens and Ones

Chapter Resources

Count on to add. Use the hundred chart to help.

1	2	3	4	5	6	7	8	9	10
11	12	13	14	15	16	17	18	19	20
21	22	23	24	25	26	27	28	29	30
31	32	33	34	35	36	37	38	39	40
41	42	43	44	45	46	47	48	49	50
51	52	53	54	55	56	57	58	59	60
61	62	63	64	65	66	67	68	69	70
71	72	73	74	75	76	77	78	79	80
81	82	83	84	85	86	87	88	89	90
91	92	93	94	95	96	97	98	99	100

45 + 20 = 65

Count on by tens to add.
45, 55, 65

21 + 3 = 24

Count on by ones to add.
21, 22, 23

Count on to add. Write the sum.

1. 18 + 30 = ______ Count by tens. 18, 28, 38, ______

2. 31 + 4 = ______ Count by ones. 31, 32, 33, ______, ______

3. 65 + 3 = ______

4. 37 + 20 = ______

5. 57 + 10 = ______

6. 41 + 40 = ______

7. 21 + 8 = ______

8. 36 + 3 = ______

9. 43 + 50 = ______

10. 62 + 7 = ______

Name ______________________________

5-2

Skills Practice

2AF1.2

Count On Tens and Ones

Count on to add. Write the sum.

1. 43 + 20 = ______ 35 + 30 = ______

2. 18 + 40 = ______ 51 + 10 = ______

3.

62	24	40	13	55
+ 10	+ 30	+ 28	+ 70	+ 20

4.

20	34	5	80	48
+ 49	+ 20	+ 44	+ 11	+ 40

5.

35	20	30	36	17
+ 10	+ 53	+ 13	+ 50	+ 30

6.

44	38	60	70	57
+ 40	+ 20	+ 18	+ 23	+ 10

Solve.

7. There are 30 children in the second grade. There are 45 children in the third grade. How many children are there in all?

______ children

8. The school gets 40 new math books. They also get 32 new spelling books. How many new books do they have now?

______ books

Name ______________________________

5-3

Reteach (1)

2AF1.2, 2MR1.0

Problem-Solving Strategy: Work Backward

Chapter Resources

Mike scores 10 more points than Sara.
Sara scores 5 more points than Des does.
Des scores 6 points.
How many points does Mike score?

Step 1 **Understand**	**What do I know?** • Mike scores 10 more points than Sara. • Sara scores 5 more points than Des. • Des scores 6 points. **What do I need to find?** • How many points Mike scores.
Step 2 **Plan**	I know how many points Des scores, so I can start there and work backward.
Step 3 **Solve**	**Work backward.** • Des scores 6 points. Sara scores 5 more than Des. Sara scores 5 (+) 6 (=) ____ points. • Mike scores 10 more than Sara. Mike scores 10 (+) 11 (=) ____ points.
Step 4 **Check**	Does my answer make sense? Yes No

Name ______________________________

5-3

Reteach (2)

2AF1.2, 2MR1.0

Problem-Solving Strategy: Work Backward *(continued)*

Work backward to solve.

1. Serena wins seven more games than Lex does. Lex wins five more games than Maria does. Maria wins six games. How many games does Serena win?

   ______ games

2. In a hotdog-eating contest, Yoshi eats 10 more hotdogs than Eli does. Eli eats 6 more hotdogs than Maury. Maury eats 8 hotdogs. How many hotdogs does Yoshi eat?

   ______ hotdogs

3. In a beanbag toss, Ruby scores 40 more points than Clare. Clare scores 30 more points than Anna, and Anna scores 20 points. How many points does Ruby score?

   ______ points

4. At the zoo today, forty more people watch the lions than the bears. Twenty more people watch the bears than the seals. Twenty people watch the seals. How many people watch the lions?

   ______ people

5. Juan collects 14 more leaves than Mia for science class. Mia collects 12 more leaves than Max. Max collects 9 leaves. How many leaves does Juan collect?

   ______ leaves

Name ______________________________

5-3

Skills Practice

2AF1.2, 2MR1.0

Problem-Solving Strategy: Work Backward

Solve. Work backward. Show your work.

1. Ann's dog does 4 more tricks than Ben's dog. Ben's dog does 9 more tricks than Lisa's dog. Lisa's dog does 5 tricks. How many tricks does Ann's dog do?

   ____

   ______ tricks

2. Green Stable has 12 more horses than Happy Glen. Happy Glen has 9 more horses than Sun Farm. Sun Farm has 7 horses. How many horses does Green Stable have?

   ____

   ______ horses

3. Dan has twenty fish in five different tanks. Ahmal has eight more fish than Dan. Their friend Andi has ten more fish than Ahmal. How many fish does Andi have?

   ____

   ______ fish

4. In one week, Kitty Rescue saves 12 cats. That same week, Caring Paws saves 6 more cats than Kitty Rescue. Here Kitty Kitty saves 10 more cats than Caring Paws. How many cats did Here Kitty Kitty save?

   ____

   ______ cats

5. Dora's Diner has 3 more breakfast specials than the Tip-Top Grill. The Tip-Top Grill has 11 more breakfast specials than Charlie's Cafe. Charlie's Cafe has 6 breakfast specials. How many breakfast specials does Dora's Diner have?

   ____

   ______ specials

Name ______________________________

5-4

Reteach

2AF1.0, 2MR1.2

Regroup Ones as Tens

Chapter Resources

Add. Regroup when you have 10 ones.

Step 1

$$\begin{array}{r} 18 \\ +\ 6 \\ \hline \end{array}$$

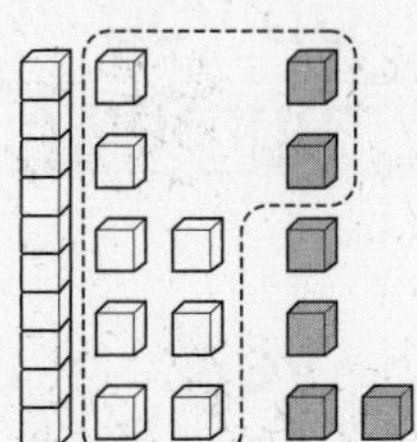

Add the ones.

___ ones = ___ ten ___ ones

Step 2

$$\begin{array}{r} 18 \\ +\ 6 \\ \hline \end{array}$$

Add the tens.

Add. Regroup when you have 10 ones.

Step 1

1. $$\begin{array}{r} 24 \\ +\ 7 \\ \hline \end{array}$$

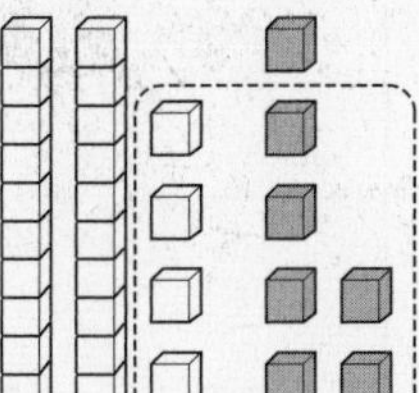

Add the ones.

___ ones = ___ ten ___ one

Step 2

$$\begin{array}{r} 24 \\ +\ 7 \\ \hline \end{array}$$

Add the tens.

2. $$\begin{array}{r} 36 \\ +\ 6 \\ \hline \end{array}$$

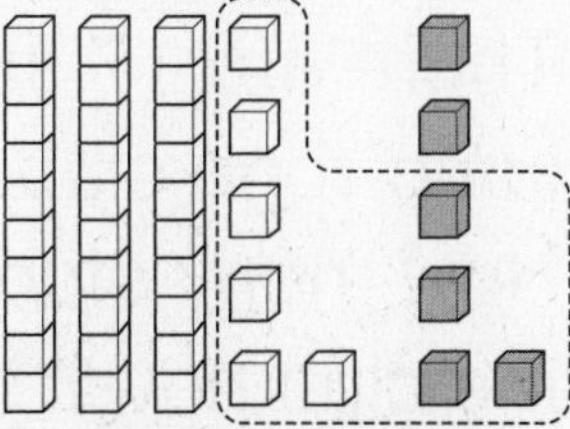

Add the ones.

___ ones = ___ ten ___ ones

$$\begin{array}{r} 36 \\ +\ 6 \\ \hline \end{array}$$

Add the tens.

Name ____________________

5-4

Skills Practice

2AF1.0, 2MR1.2

Regroup Ones as Tens

Use WorkMat 6 and [tens rod] to add.

		Add the ones. Add the tens.	Do you regroup?	Write the sum.
1.	15 + 7	1 tens 12 ones	yes no	15 + 7
2.	34 + 6	____ tens ____ ones	yes no	34 + 6
3.	52 + 7	____ tens ____ ones	yes no	52 + 7
4.	73 + 5	____ tens ____ ones	yes no	73 + 5

Solve.

5. Sam has 93 stamps. Len gives him 4 more. How many stamps does Sam have now?

______ stamps

6. There are 17 students in the jump-rope club. 8 more join. How many students are in the club now?

______ students

5-5

Name ______________________

Reteach

2AF1.0, 2MR1.2

Add One-Digit Numbers and Two-Digit Numbers

Chapter Resources

Find the sum. Regroup if you need to.

Step 1

16
+ 6

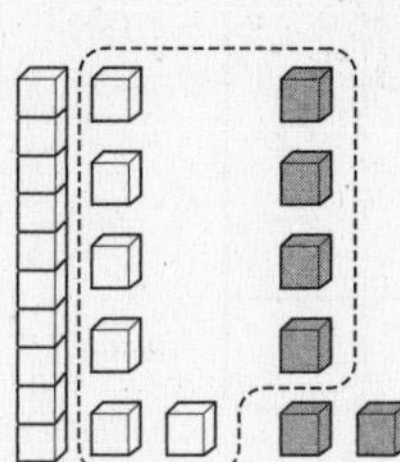

Add the ones.

___ ones = ___ ten ___ ones

Step 2

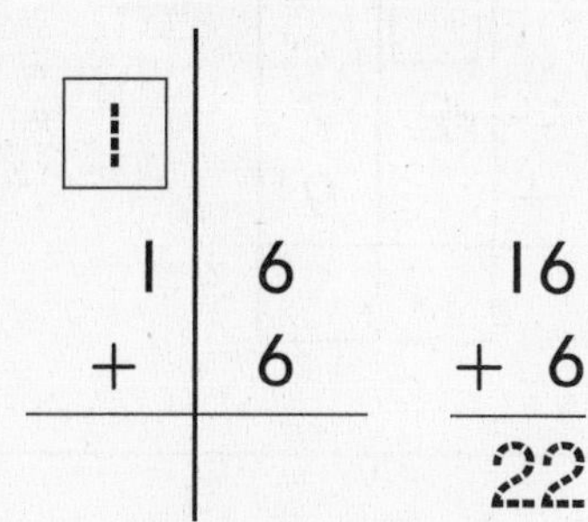

Add the tens.

Add. Shade 10 ones. Regroup if you need to.

Step 1

1. 35
+ 6

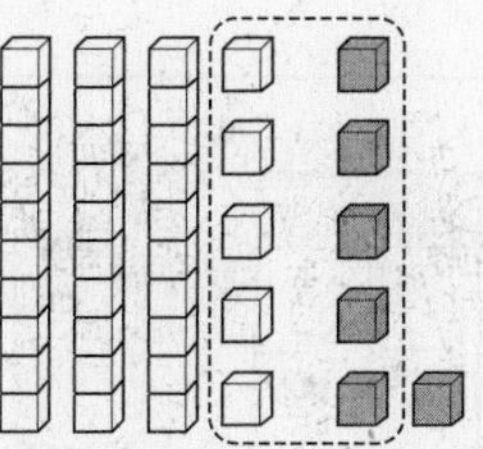

Add the ones.

___ ones = ___ ten ___ one

Step 2

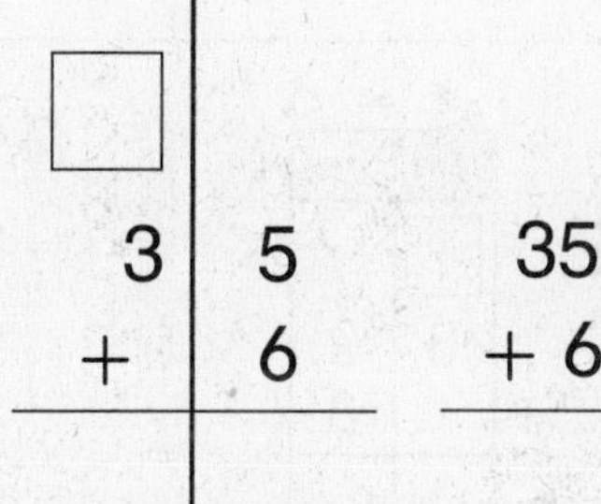

Add the tens.

2. 24
+ 9

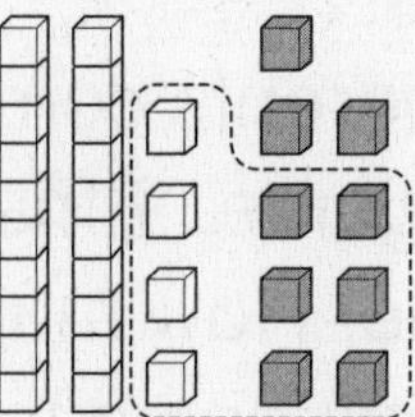

Add the ones.

___ ones = ___ ten ___ ones

[ ]			
	2	4	24
+		9	+ 9

Add the tens.

5-5

Name ______________________________

Skills Practice

2AF1.0, 2MR1.2

Add One-Digit Numbers and Two-Digit Numbers

Use WorkMat 6 and 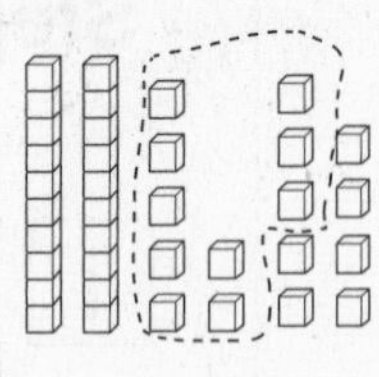 **to add.**

1.

tens	ones
2	7
+	9

2.

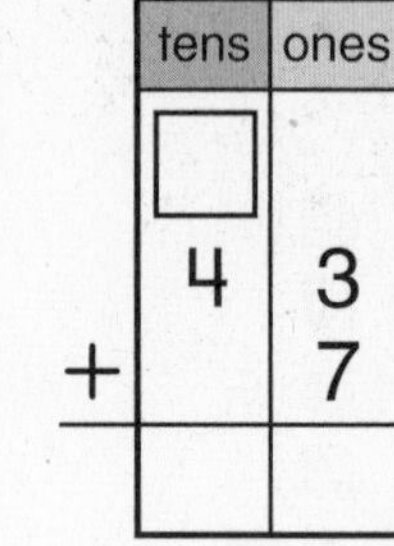

tens	ones
4	3
+	7

3.

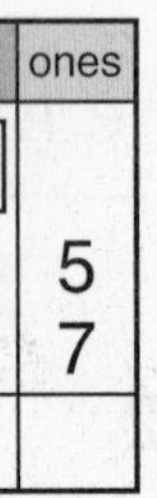

tens	ones
5	5
+	7

4.

tens	ones
5	4
+	8

5.

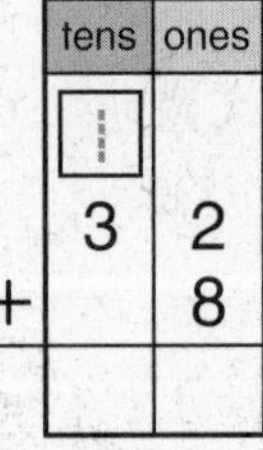

tens	ones
3	2
+	8

6.

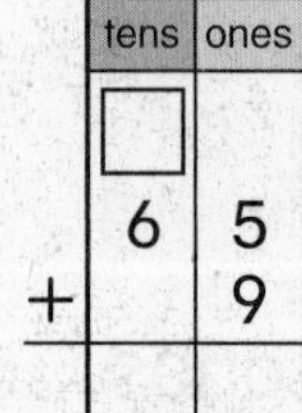

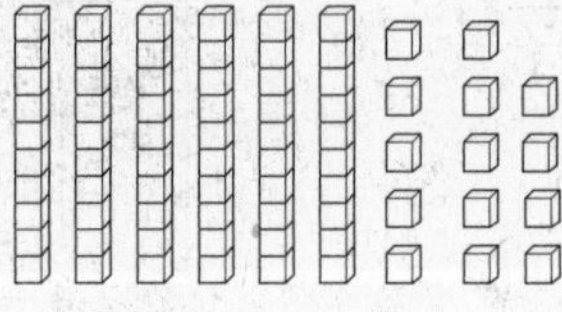

tens	ones
6	5
+	9

Solve.

7. Jana scores 18 points in the first half of a game. She scores 6 more points in the second half. How many points does she score in all?

_______ points

8. 22 parents come to watch the game. 9 friends also come. How many total people come to watch the game?

_______ people

5-6

Name ____________________

Reteach

2NS2.2, 2AF1.3

Add Two-Digit Numbers

Preparation: A set of counters is needed for this activity.

June has 28 stickers.
Pam gives her 16 more stickers.
How many stickers does June have now?

Step 1

28
+16

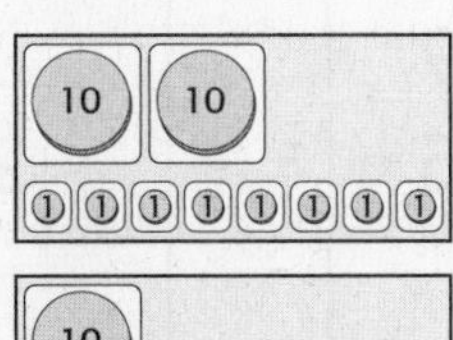

Step 2

Regroup 10 ones as 1 ten if you can.

Step 3

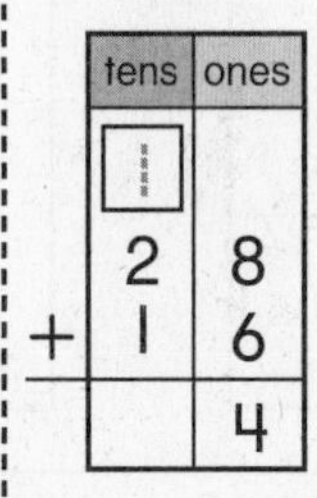

28
+16
44

June has 44 stickers.

Add. You can use counters to help. Regroup if you need to.

1.

tens	ones
□	
3	7
+ 2	7

tens	ones
□	
3	5
+ 1	5

tens	ones
□	
4	8
+ 2	5

tens	ones
□	
1	4
+ 2	3

2.

tens	ones
□	
1	9
+ 6	8

tens	ones
□	
3	6
+ 4	3

tens	ones
□	
5	4
+ 2	7

tens	ones
□	
3	8
+ 2	9

Name ______________________

5-6

Skills Practice

Add Two-Digit Numbers

2NS2.2, 2AF1.3

Preparation: Base-ten blocks are needed for this activity.

Use WorkMat 6 and [ten-rod] to add.

1.

tens	ones
1	
2	5
+ 1	7

tens	ones
2	4
+ 1	2

tens	ones
3	9
+ 2	5

tens	ones
2	2
+ 2	8

2.

tens	ones
1	
4	9
+ 1	8

tens	ones
2	4
+ 4	9

tens	ones
2	4
+ 3	1

tens	ones
4	6
+ 3	9

Solve.

3. 46 people come to the museum in the morning. 39 more people come in the afternoon. How many people come to the museum?

______ people

4. 20 people go on a tour of the factory in the morning. 17 go on a tour in the afternoon. How many people go on a tour in all?

______ people

Name ______________________

5-7

Reteach

2NS6.0, 2NS2.0

Estimate Sums

Chapter Resources

An estimate is an answer that is close to the exact answer.
If you do not need an exact answer, you can estimate.

1	2	3	4	5	6	7	8	9	**10**
11	12	13	(14)	15	16	17	18	19	**20**
21	22	23	24	25	26	(27)	28	29	**30**
31	32	33	34	35	36	37	38	39	**40**
41	42	43	44	45	46	47	48	49	**50**
51	52	53	54	55	56	57	58	59	**60**
61	62	63	64	65	66	67	68	69	**70**
71	72	73	74	75	76	77	78	79	**80**
81	82	83	84	85	86	87	88	89	**90**
91	92	93	94	95	96	97	98	99	**100**

$$\begin{array}{r} 27 \\ +\ 14 \\ \hline 41 \end{array} \rightarrow \begin{array}{r} 30 \\ +\ 10 \\ \hline 40 \end{array}$$

Think about which ten each addend is closer to.

27 is closer to <u>30</u>. 14 is closer to <u>10</u>.

27 + 14 is about <u>40</u>.

41 is close to 40, so the answer is reasonable.

Round each addend to the nearest ten.
Estimate the sum.

1. 45 + 14 = 59 → 50 + 10 = 60

2. 82 + 12 = 94 → ____ + ____

3. 76 + 12 = 88 → ____ + ____

4. 31 + 28 = 59 → ____ + ____

5. 38 + 28 = 66 → ____ + ____

6. 16 + 49 = 65 → ____ + ____

7. 47 + 29 = 76 → ____ + ____

8. 12 + 59 = 71 → ____ + ____

9. 83 + 16 = 99 → ____ + ____

Name ______________________________

5-7

Skills Practice

2NS6.0, 2NS2.0

Estimate Sums

You can estimate when you don't need an exact answer, or to check addition. A number line can help you estimate.

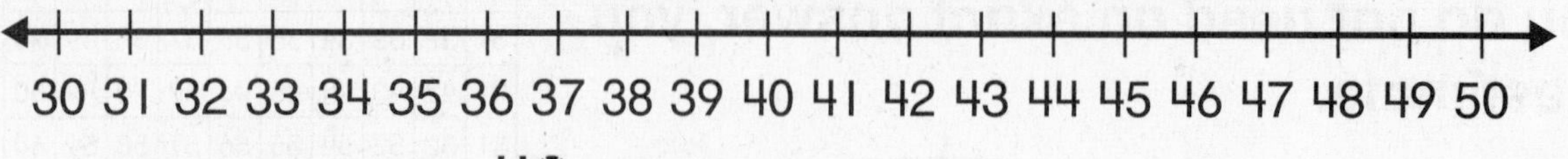

37 is closer to <u>40</u>.

28 is closer to <u>30</u>.

40 + 30 is <u>70</u>.

37	→	40
+ 28	→	+ 30
65		70

37 + 28 = <u>65</u>

65 is close to 70, so the answer is reasonable.

Add. Then round each addend to the nearest ten. Estimate the sum.

1.			**2.**			**3.**		
28	→	30	38	→		32	→	
+ 28	→	+ 30	+ 49	→	+ ____	+ 41	→	+ ____
56		60						

4.		**5.**		**6.**	
48		31		22	
+ 33	+ ____	+ 32	+ ____	+ 48	+ ____

Solve. Make an estimate.

7. Hugo has 43 cents. Olive has 48 cents. Together, do they have enough to buy a box of raisins that costs 85 cents? Prove your answer.

____

8. Kendra has 27 cents. Mikey has 43 cents. Do they have enough money to buy a box of popcorn that costs 90 cents? Explain.

____

5-8

Name ______________________

Reteach

2AF1.1, 2MR3.0

Add Three Two-Digit Numbers

Chapter Resources

You can use addition strategies to help you add three addends.

Look for doubles.

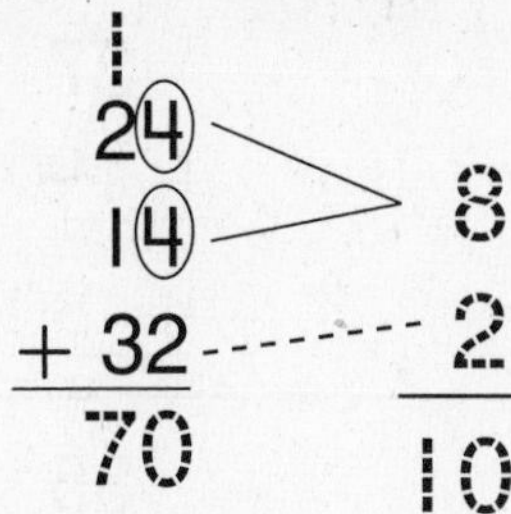

Look for a ten.

37
11
+ 33
81

10
1
11

Add. Circle the doubles. Put a box on the tens.

1.	14	42	27	29	24	48
	24	27	10	42	11	11
	+ 13	+ 12	+ 13	+ 21	+ 26	+ 12
	51					
2.	17	23	45	6	10	23
	30	26	13	24	57	16
	+ 13	+ 46	+ 15	+ 40	+ 23	+ 33
3.	32	13	55	19	37	21
	18	36	20	41	17	17
	+ 11	+ 46	+ 15	+ 13	+ 32	+ 13

Name ___________________________________

5-8

Skills Practice

2AF1.1, 2MR3.0

Add Three Two-Digit Numbers

Look for two numbers in the ones column that make a ten or a double. Circle them. Add.

1.

23	41	35	13	26
14	32	18	24	37
+ 27	+ 12	+ 25	+ 4	+ 14
64				

2.

8	36	55	11	35
20	28	13	63	16
+ 12	+ 32	+ 14	+ 24	+ 34

3.

14	52	44	19	24
18	20	16	68	3
+ 14	+ 11	+ 22	+ 12	+ 25

4.

21	37	14	62	43
18	13	45	11	15
+ 21	+ 27	+ 3	+ 23	+ 22

Solve.

5. There are 34 children in first grade. There are 27 in second grade. There are 31 in third grade. How many children are there in all?

______ children

6. 13 students play the bells. 16 students play the drums. 24 students play the recorder. How many total students play instruments?

______ students

Name ______________________________

5-9

Reteach (1)

2MR1.1, 2AF1.2

Problem-Solving Investigation: Choose a Strategy

Chapter Resources

On a math test, Edie scores 10 points more than Jack. Jack's score is 5 points more than Dee's. Dee scores 73 points. How many points does Edie score?

Step 1 Understand

What do I know?

Edie scores __10__ more points than Jack.

Jack scores __5__ more points than Dee.

Dee scores 73 points.

What do I need to find?

How many points __Edie__ scores.

Step 2 Plan

How will I find how many?

I can __write__ a number sentence.

Step 3 Solve

Write a number sentence.

Jack scores __5__ more than Dee.

Edie scores __10__ more points than Jack.

Edie's score is __10__ + __5__ + __73__.

__10__ + __5__ + __73__ = __88__

Edie scored __88__ points.

Step 4 Check

Did I write a number sentence? __yes__

Does my answer make sense? __yes__

Name ______________________________

5-9

Reteach (2)

2MR1.1, 2AF1.2

Problem-Solving Investigation: Choose a Strategy

Problem-Solving Strategies
- Draw a Picture
- Work Backward
- Write a Number Sentence

Solve.

1. The school has three buses. 34 children ride on one bus. 27 children ride on the second bus. 33 children ride on the third bus. How many children ride in all?

   ______ children

2. Jesse's bus takes 16 minutes to school. Miguel's bus takes 17 more minutes to get to school. Jo's bus takes 20 more minutes to get to school. How many minutes does it take Jo's bus to get to school?

   ______ minutes

Number of Visitors to the Art Exhibit			
Visitor	Friday	Saturday	Sunday
Children	21	43	19
Adults	18	51	28

3. On what day did the art exhibit have the most visitors? Tell how you know.

   ____

   ____

4. Who visited the art exhibit more, adults or children? Tell how you know.

   ____

Name ______________________________

5-9

Skills Practice

2MR1.1, 2AF1.2

Problem-Solving Investigation: Choose a Strategy

Chapter Resources

Problem-Solving Strategies
- Draw a Picture
- Work Backward
- Write a Number Sentence

Solve.

1. Mr. Garcia's class buys tickets for the basketball game. They buy 27 children's tickets and 35 adult tickets. The team also gives them 30 free tickets. How many tickets does the class have in all?

   ______ tickets

2. At the game there are 18 band members in red. 22 band members wear blue and 31 wear white. How many band members are there in all?

   ______ band members

3. At the snack stand, Tony sells 34 bags of popcorn. He sells 25 drinks and 32 hotdogs. How many snacks does he sell in all?

   ______ snacks

4. Cheryl scores 28 points. Jia scores 12 points more than Cheryl does. Brooke scores 18 more points than Jia. How many points does Brooke score?

   ______ points

Name ______________________________

6-1

Reteach

2MR3.0, 2NS2.3

Subtract Tens

Preparation: Glue and scissors are necessary for this activity.

5 − 2 = 3

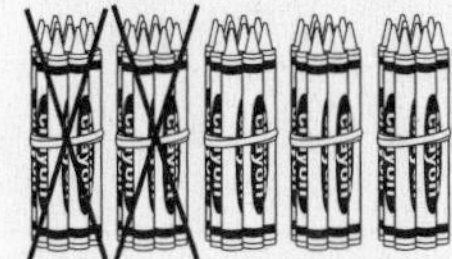

50 − 20 = 30

You can use basic facts to help subtract tens.
5 − 2 = 3 helps you know that 50 − 20 = 30.

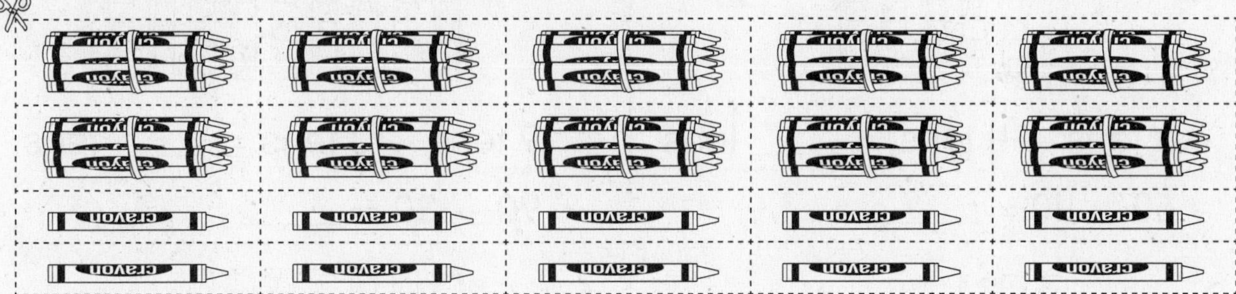

Cut out the squares. Glue them to match the problems.

1. 3 − 2 = ______

2. 30 − 20 = ______

3. 50 − 30 = ______

4. 40 − 10 = ______

5. 70 − 20 = ______

6. 60 − 30 = ______

7. 80 − 40 = ______

8. 90 − 10 = ______

6-1

Name ______________________________

Skills Practice

2MR3.0, 2NS2.3

Subtract Tens

Subtract tens.

1. 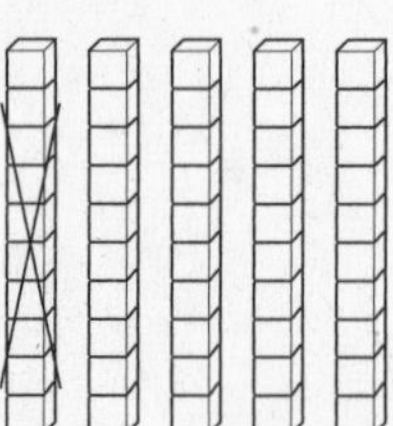

5 tens − 1 ten = 4 tens

50 − 10 = 40

2. 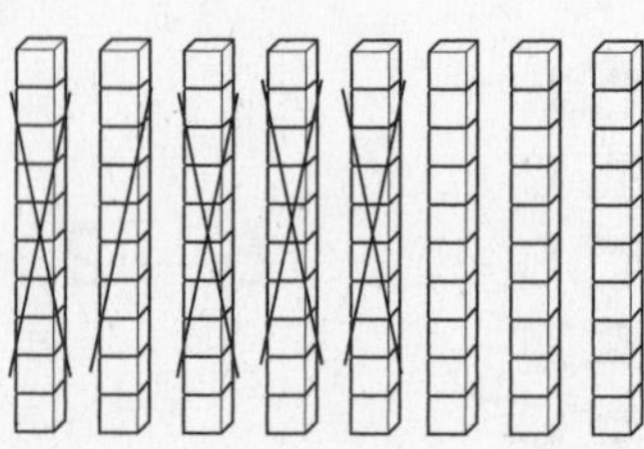

8 tens − 5 tens = _____ tens

80 − 50 = _____

3. 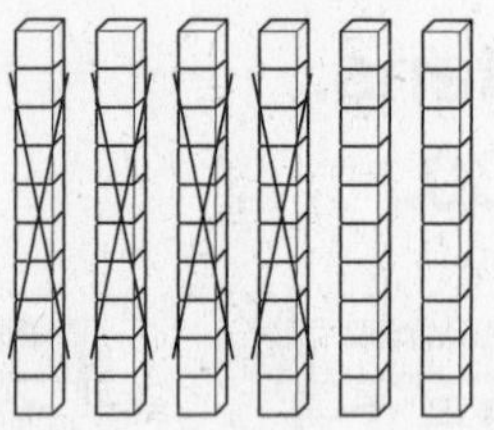

6 tens − 4 tens = _____ tens

60 − 40 = _____

4. 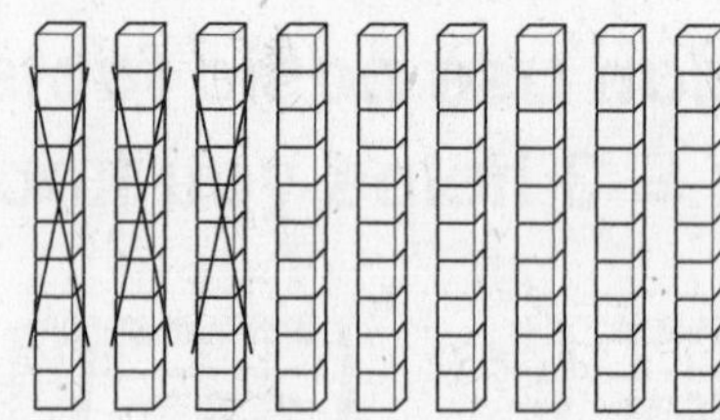

9 tens − 3 tens = _____ tens

90 − 30 = _____

5. 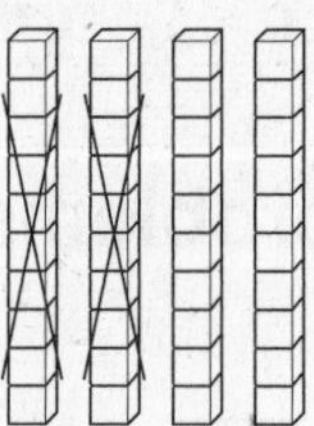

4 tens − 2 tens = _____ tens

40 − 20 = _____

6. 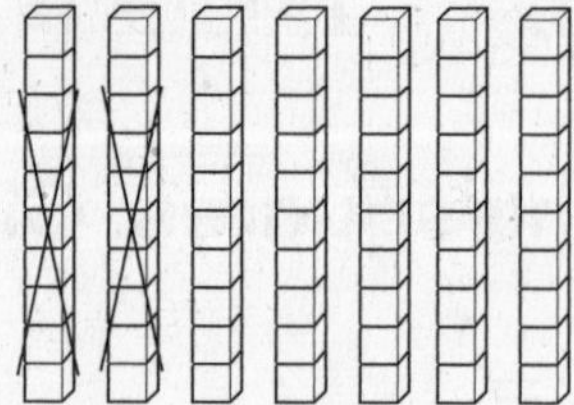

7 tens − 2 tens = _____ tens

70 − 20 = _____

Solve.

7. What is 2 tens from 7 tens? _____ − _____ = _____

8. What is 3 tens from 5 tens? _____ − _____ = _____

Name ______________________

6-2

Reteach

2AF1.0

Count Back Tens and Ones

4 – 3 = ?

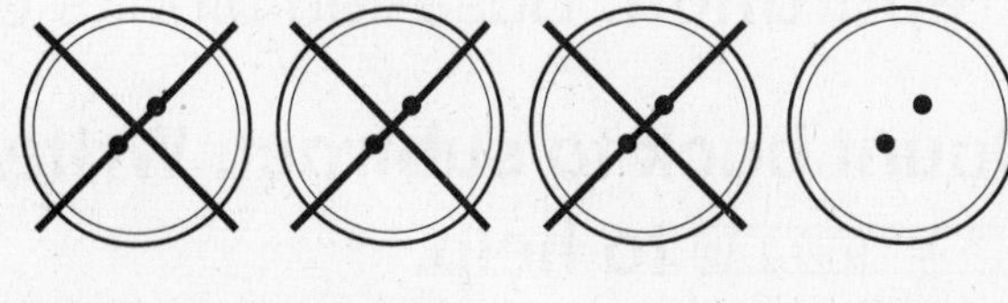

Count back by ones to subtract.

3, 2, 1, . . . 4 – 3 = 1

40 – 30 = ?

Count back by tens to subtract ten.

30, 20, 10 . . . 40 – 30 = 10

Subtract. Cross out the buttons as you count back. Write your answer.

1. 46 – 4 = ______ **2.** 39 – 20 = ______

3. 77 – 40 = ______ **4.** 57 – 5 = ______

5. 53 – 20 = ______ **6.** 48 – 7 = ______

7. 65 – 40 = ______ **8.** 71 – 30 = ______

9. 37 – 4 = ______ **10.** 52 – 10 = ______

Chapter Resources

Name ______________________

6-2

Skills Practice

2AF1.0

Count Back Tens and Ones

Preparation: Base-ten blocks are necessary for this activity.

Count back to subtract. Write the difference. Use [ten-rod] to help.

1.	28 − 5	64 − 30	36 − 4	52 − 10	45 − 2
2.	61 − 40	68 − 2	75 − 50	89 − 20	37 − 3
3.	54 − 1	65 − 40	32 − 10	60 − 3	26 − 10
4.	70 − 30	45 − 20	72 − 2	55 − 4	82 − 60

Solve.

5. Lauren has five dimes in her pocket. She spends two of them. How much money does she have left? ______ cents

6. Alex has six dimes and seven pennies. He spends four pennies. How much money does he have left? ______ cents

7. What is 3 tens from 9 tens? ______ − ______ = ______

8. What is 4 tens from 5 tens? ______ − ______ = ______

Name ______________________

6-3

Reteach

2AF1.0, 2MR1.2

Regroup Tens as Ones

Chapter Resources

Candy had 32 markers. She gives six to Ray.
How many markers does she have left?

32 − 6 = ?

To help solve this problem, you can regroup one box of markers as ten markers.

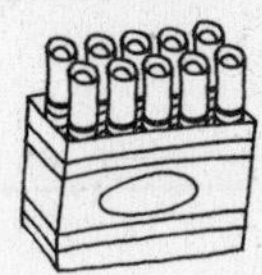 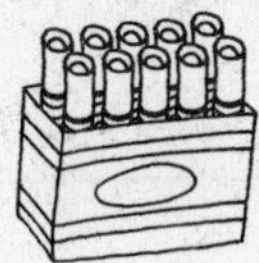  = 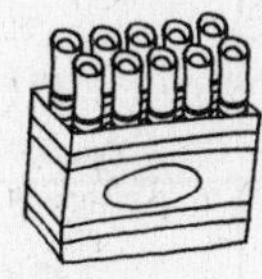 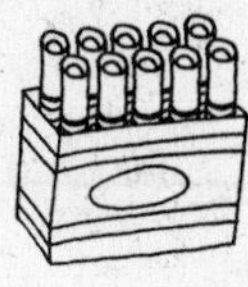

Now there are enough markers. Subtract.

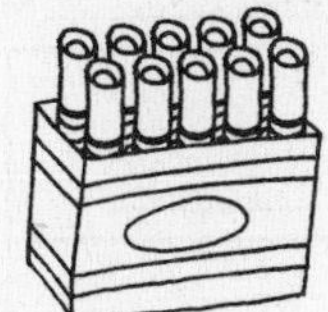 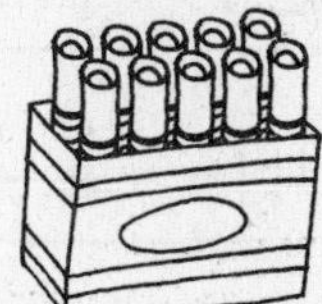 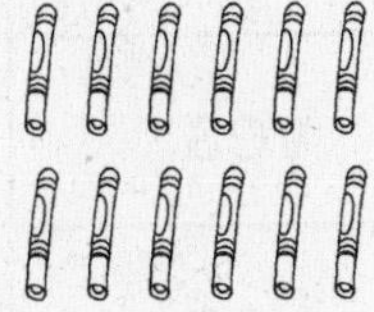

32 − 6 = ______. Candy has 26 markers left.

Write the number sentences. Use [tens rod]. Regroup if needed. Then solve.

1. Jim had 52 posters. He sold 18 of them.
How many posters does he have now?

______ − ______ = ______

2. Ellen had 34 crayons. She gives 5 to her friends.
How many does she have left?

______ − ______ = ______

3. John had 41 pennies. He spent 15 of them.
How many pennies does he have now?

______ − ______ = ______

Name ______________________________

6-3

Skills Practice

2AF1.0, 2MR1.2

Regroup Tens as Ones

Use WorkMat 6 and [tens rod] to subtract.

	Do you need more ones to subtract?	Write the difference.
1. 32 − 5	no yes	32 − 5 = ______
2. 27 − 8	no yes	27 − 8 = ______
3. 28 − 5	no yes	28 − 5 = ______
4. 55 − 7	no yes	55 − 7 = ______
5. 41 − 6	no yes	41 − 6 = ______
6. 36 − 9	no yes	36 − 9 = ______

Solve.

7. Brian has 42 trading cards. He gives seven to a friend. How many trading cards does Brian have left?

______ trading cards

8. Sam has 33 cents. He spends 15 at the store. How much money does he have left?

______ cents

Name ______________________________

6-4

Reteach (1)

2AF1.2, 2MR1.0

Problem-Solving Strategy: Write a Number Sentence

Chapter Resources

There are eight bats in a tower.
Three more join them.
How many bats are now in the tower?

Step 1 **Understand**	**What do I know?** There are eight bats. Three more join them. **What do I need to find out?** How many bats there are now.
Step 2 **Plan**	**How will I find out how many bats there are in all?** I know the number of bats in the tower. I know the number of bats that join them. A number sentence would tell me how many there are. I would subtract if some bats left the tower. But no bats left the tower. I will write a number sentence and ______.
Step 3 **Solve**	**Write an addition sentence.** 8 (+) 3 (=) 11 bats
Step 4 **Check**	What were the two groups in my addition sentence? Did my answer tell how many bats there are in all? 

6-4

Name ______________________________

Reteach (2)

2AF1.2, 2MR1.0

Problem-Solving Strategy: Write a Number Sentence

Write a number sentence to solve.

1. Spot has 13 bones in his doghouse. He found four more in the yard. How many bones does Spot have?

   ____ ◯ ____ ◯ ____

   ____ bones

2. Lu sees 17 rabbits in a field. She sees six more in the woods.

   How many rabbits does she see in all?

   ____ ◯ ____ ◯ ____

   ____ rabbits

3. Twenty-one monkeys are in the tree. Five monkeys swing away. How many monkeys are left?

   ____ ◯ ____ ◯ ____

   ____ monkeys

4. Thirteen crows are in a cornfield. Six fly away. How many crows are left?

   ____ ◯ ____ ◯ ____

   ____ crows

5. Kay finds six shells. Then she finds nine more. How many shells did she find in all?

   ____ ◯ ____ ◯ ____

   ____ shells

6. Joey catches 18 fish. His family keeps four of them. How many fish did they let go?

   ____ ◯ ____ ◯ ____

   ____ fish

Name ______________________________

6-4

Skills Practice

2AF1.2, 2MR1.0

Problem-Solving Strategy: Write a Number Sentence

Chapter Resources

Write a number sentence to solve.

1. Seven kids are in the sandbox. Six more are on the swings. How many kids are there in all?

_____ ◯ _____ ◯

_____ kids

2. Erica colors 15 pictures. She gives 11 to her family. How many pictures are left?

_____ ◯ _____ ◯

_____ pictures

3. Ben ran 11 miles. Jeff ran 5 miles. How many more miles did Ben run?

_____ ◯ _____ ◯

_____ miles

4. Roland mows lawns. He made 22 dollars the first week. He made 7 dollars the next. How much money did he make?

_____ ◯ _____ ◯

_____ dollars

5. Nine chickens are eating. Fourteen more chickens join them. How many chickens are eating now?

_____ ◯ _____ ◯

_____ chickens

6. Jesse buys 16 game cards. He gives 4 to his friends. How many cards does Jesse have left?

_____ ◯ _____ ◯

_____ cards

Name ____________________

6-5

Reteach

2AF1.0, 2MR2.1

Subtract One-Digit Numbers from Two-Digit Numbers

Chapter Resources

Find 42 – 8.

tens	ones
4 tens	2 ones

Show 42.
Can you subtract 8 ones?
Regroup 1 ten as 10 ones.
Now there are 3 tens and 12 ones.

```
 3 12
  4 2
–   8
```

Use WorkMat 6 and [ten rod] to subtract.

1.

tens	ones
☐	☐
5	3
–	9

2.

tens	ones
☐	☐
3	4
–	6

3.

tens	ones
☐	☐
4	7
–	8

4. 25 – 7 = ____

5. 81 – 8 = ____

6. 54 – 9 = ____

7. 62 – 3 = ____

8. 76 – 4 = ____

9. 33 – 6 = ____

Name ______

6-5

Skills Practice

2AF1.0, 2MR2.1

Subtract One-Digit Numbers from Two-Digit Numbers

Use WorkMat 6 and [ten-rod] to subtract.

1.

tens	ones
1	13
2	3
−	9
1	4

tens	ones
3	6
−	9

tens	ones
4	1
−	5

tens	ones
5	8
−	6

2.

tens	ones
4	6
−	7

tens	ones
5	2
−	6

tens	ones
3	7
−	9

tens	ones
6	5
−	8

3. Gary has 72 cents. He spends eight cents. How much does he have now?

______ cents

4. There are 55 mice in the barn. A cat chases nine of them away. How many mice are left?

______ mice

Name ____________________

6-6

Reteach

2AF1.0, 2NS2.0

Subtract Two-Digit Numbers

Chapter Resources

Find 36 − 17.

tens	ones
3 tens	6 ones

Show 36.
Can you subtract 7 ones?
Regroup 1 ten as 10 ones.
Now there are 2 tens and
16 ones.

$$\begin{array}{r} \boxed{2}\ \boxed{16} \\ \not{3}\not{6} \\ -\ 1\ 7 \\ \hline \end{array}$$

Use WorkMat 6 and [ten rod] to subtract.

1.

tens	ones
☐	☐
8	0
− 3	6

2.

tens	ones
☐	☐
6	5
− 2	7

3.

tens	ones
☐	☐
4	7
− 1	9

---

4. 29 − 15 = ____

5. 41 − 18 = ____

6. 63 − 38 = ____

7. 76 − 49 = ____

8. 54 − 25 = ____

9. 32 − 16 = ____

Name ______________________

6-6

Skills Practice

2AF1.0, 2NS2.0

Subtract Two-Digit Numbers

Use WorkMat 6 and [tens rod] to subtract.

1.

tens	ones
4	15
5	5
− 1	7
3	8

tens	ones
4	5
− 1	2

tens	ones
3	1
−	7

tens	ones
6	2
− 1	8

2.

tens	ones
4	5
− 2	9

tens	ones
2	8
− 1	2

tens	ones
5	6
− 2	7

tens	ones
7	4
− 7	0

3. Phoebe makes 52 cookies for the bake sale. She sells 36 of them. How many cookies are leftover?

______ cookies

4. There are 41 pumpkins in the field. The farmer sold 17 of them. How many pumpkins are left?

______ pumpkins

Name ______________________________

6-7

Reteach

2NS2.1, 2MR2.2

Check Subtraction

Chapter Resources

Find 32 − 14.

tens	ones
2	12
~~3~~	~~2~~
− 1	4
1	8

Is this answer correct?
check by adding.

$$\begin{array}{r} {}^{1}\\ 18 \\ +\ 14 \\ \hline 32 \end{array}$$

Subtract. Then check by adding.

1. $\begin{array}{r} 16 \\ -\ 5 \\ \hline 11 \end{array}$ $\begin{array}{r} 11 \\ +\ 5 \\ \hline 16 \end{array}$

2. $\begin{array}{r} 53 \\ -\ 18 \\ \hline \end{array}$ $\begin{array}{r} \\ +\ 18 \\ \hline \end{array}$

3. $\begin{array}{r} 93 \\ -\ 38 \\ \hline \end{array}$ $\begin{array}{r} \\ +\ 38 \\ \hline \end{array}$

4. $\begin{array}{r} 46 \\ -\ 23 \\ \hline \end{array}$ $\begin{array}{r} \\ +\ 23 \\ \hline \end{array}$

5. $\begin{array}{r} 84 \\ -\ 57 \\ \hline \end{array}$ $\begin{array}{r} \\ +\ 57 \\ \hline \end{array}$

6. $\begin{array}{r} 75 \\ -\ 49 \\ \hline \end{array}$ $\begin{array}{r} \\ +\ 49 \\ \hline \end{array}$

Name ______________________________

6-7

Skills Practice

2NS2.1, 2MR2.2

Check Subtraction

Subtract. Then check by adding.

1. $\begin{array}{r} 65 \\ -\ 21 \\ \hline 44 \end{array}$ $\begin{array}{r} 44 \\ +\ 21 \\ \hline 65 \end{array}$ | $\begin{array}{r} 37 \\ -\ 14 \\ \hline \end{array}$ $\begin{array}{r} \\ +\ \quad \\ \hline \end{array}$ | $\begin{array}{r} 43 \\ -\ 25 \\ \hline \end{array}$ $\begin{array}{r} \\ +\ \quad \\ \hline \end{array}$

2. $\begin{array}{r} 71 \\ -\ 7 \\ \hline \end{array}$ $\begin{array}{r} \\ +\ \quad \\ \hline \end{array}$ | $\begin{array}{r} 54 \\ -\ 36 \\ \hline \end{array}$ $\begin{array}{r} \\ +\ \quad \\ \hline \end{array}$ | $\begin{array}{r} 81 \\ -\ 34 \\ \hline \end{array}$ $\begin{array}{r} \\ +\ \quad \\ \hline \end{array}$

3. $\begin{array}{r} 95 \\ -\ 23 \\ \hline \end{array}$ $\begin{array}{r} \\ +\ \quad \\ \hline \end{array}$ | $\begin{array}{r} 63 \\ -\ 9 \\ \hline \end{array}$ $\begin{array}{r} \\ +\ \quad \\ \hline \end{array}$ | $\begin{array}{r} 48 \\ -\ 19 \\ \hline \end{array}$ $\begin{array}{r} \\ +\ \quad \\ \hline \end{array}$

Solve. Check by adding.

4. Students in Mr. Frank's class made 10 pictures. They showed 6 at the art fair. How many were not shown?

   ______ pictures

5. Mr. Levine is 53 years old. Mr. Smith is 37 years old. How much older is Mr. Levine?

   ______ years older

Name ______________________________

6-8

Reteach (1)

2MR1.1, 2AF1.0

Problem-Solving Investigation: Choose a Strategy

Mildred Mouse counted 18 holes in one piece of cheese. She counted 31 holes in the other piece of cheese. How many holes are there in all?

Step 1 **Understand**	**What do I know?** There are 18 holes in one piece of cheese. There are 31 holes in the other piece of cheese. **What do I need to find out?** How many holes are there?
Step 2 **Plan**	**How will I find out?** I can draw a picture to find out how many holes there are. But that would take a long time. I can write a number sentence. But it might be easier to use a model. I can use a model.
Step 3 **Solve**	**Use a model.** There are ______ holes.
Step 4 **Check**	Does my model show how many holes there are? Can I use my model to check my work?

Name ______________________________

6-8

Reteach (2)

2MR1.1, 2AF1.0

Problem-Solving Investigation: Choose a Strategy

- Write a number sentence.
- Draw a picture.
- Use a model.

Choose a strategy and solve.

1. 55 girls and 36 boys play volleyball. How many more girls than boys play volleyball?

   ______ more girls

2. There are 48 cows in the field. There are 23 in the barn. How many cows are there?

   ______ cows

Use the chart for Exercises 3 and 4.

Swimmer	Number of Laps
Dan	22
Sandy	18
Alan	45

3. During swimming practice, how many laps did Dan and Sandy swim?

   ______ laps

4. How many more laps did Alan swim than Sandy?

   ______ more laps

Name ______________________________

6-8

Skills Practice

2MR1.1, 2AF1.0

Problem-Solving Investigation: Choose a Strategy

- Write a number sentence.
- Draw a picture.
- Use a model.

Choose a strategy and solve.

1. There are 18 frogs in the pond.
   There are five frogs in the grass.
   How many frogs are there?

   ______ frogs

2. Together, Jamie and Alex picked 72 berries.
   Jamie picked 32. How many did Alex pick?

   ______ berries

3. There are 10 boys and 17 girls at the mall.
   How many kids are there?

   ______ kids

4. Ian has five sets of 10 crayons.
   He gives three crayons from each set to his brother.
   How many crayons does Ian have left?

   ______ crayons

Name ______________________________

6-9

Reteach

2NS2.0, 2NS2.3

Estimate Differences

Chapter Resources

In the problem below, you need to know <u>about</u> how many peanuts are left. You need to make a good guess. A guess is also called an estimate. You can estimate when you do not need an exact answer.

There are 18 peanuts in the pile. Edna the elephant eats 9 of them. About how many peanuts are left?

Step 1: Round each number to the nearest ten.

The number 9 is close to 10.
9 rounds to 10.

The number 18 is close to 20.
18 rounds to 20.

Step 2: Subtract the rounded numbers to find your estimate.

18 − 9 is about the same as 20 − 10.
20 − 10 = 10
18 − 9 is about ______.

Round these numbers to the nearest ten and estimate the difference.

1. 47 → 50
− 31 → − 30

2. 42 →
− 33 → − ______

3. 39 →
− 32 → − ______

4. 47 →
− 38 → − ______

Name ______________________________

6-9

Skills Practice

2NS2.0, 2NS2.3

Estimate Differences

Round each number to the nearest ten. Estimate the difference.

Round up if the number has 5, 6, 7, 8, or 9 ones. 15 rounds up to 20. Round down if the number has 4, 3, 2, or 1 ones. 14 rounds down to 10.

1. 49 – 31

50
– 30
20

2. 66 – 27

– ______

3. 77 – 31

– ______

4. 39 – 31

– ______

5. 48 – 32

– ______

6. 89 – 11

– ______

Solve.

7. Sharon spent 33 cents at the carnival. Her brother spent 19 cents. About how much more did Sharon spend?

______ cents

8. Morgan has 32 music CDs. He gives 13 to his brother. About how many music CDs does Morgan have left?

______ CDs

Name ____________________

Reteach

2NS5.0

Pennies, Nickels, and Dimes

You can skip count to find the value of pennies, nickels, and dimes.

penny 1¢
Count by ones.

nickel 5¢
Count by fives.

dime 10¢
Count by tens.

10 20 30 40 50

Circle the coins you need to buy the object.

1. 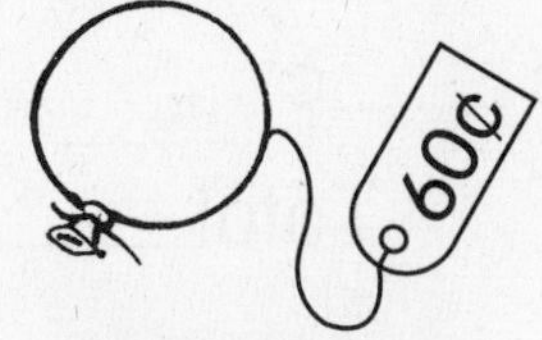

2. 

3. 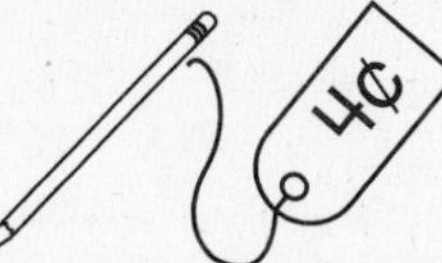

4. 

5. 

Name ______________________________

7-1

Skills Practice

2NS5.0

Pennies, Nickels, and Dimes

Count to find the value.

1.     

10 ¢ 20 ¢ ____¢ ____¢ ____¢ ____¢ ____¢ Total ____ ¢

2.         

____¢ ____¢ ____¢ ____¢ ____¢ ____¢ ____¢ ____¢ ____¢

Total ____¢

3.    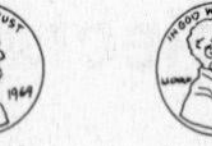     

____¢ ____¢ ____¢ ____¢ ____¢ ____¢ ____¢ ____¢

Total ____¢

4.       

____¢ ____¢ ____¢ ____¢ ____¢ ____¢ Total ____¢

Solve.

5. Jake has six dimes in his pocket.

How much money does Jake have? ______¢

6. Marcia has four dimes. Tia has six nickels.

Who has more money? ____________

7. Sue has 5 nickels. Jill has 5 dimes.

Who has more money? ____________

Name ______________________

7-2 Reteach

2NS5.0, 2MR1.2

Quarters and Half-Dollars

You can skip count to find the value of quarters and half-dollars.

quarter 25¢
Count by twenty-fives.

half dollar 50¢
Count by fifties.

25 50 75

Circle the coins you need to buy the object.

1. 

2. 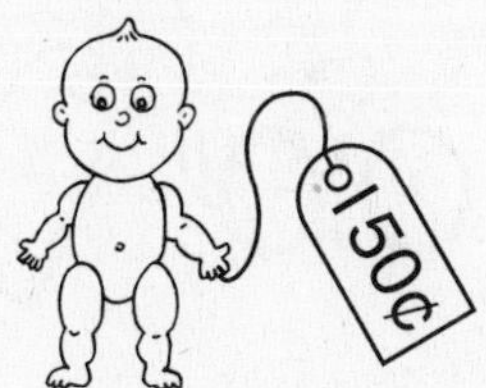

3. 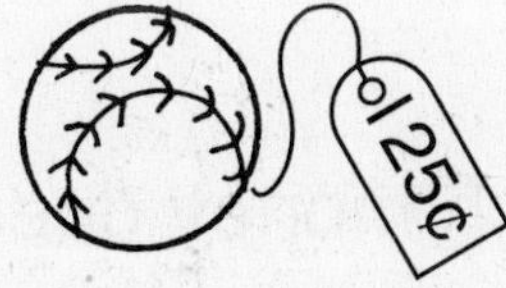

4. 

7-2

Name ______________________

Skills Practice

2NS5.0, 2MR1.2

Quarters and Half-Dollars

Count the value of the coins. Use coins to help. Then write the total in the price tag.

1.   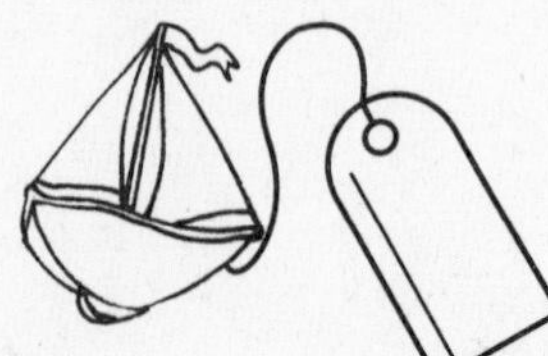

_____¢ _____¢

2.    

______¢ ______¢ ______¢

3.      

______¢ ______¢ ______¢ ______¢ ______¢

4.       

______¢ ______¢ ______¢ ______¢ ______¢ ______¢

Solve.

5. Peg has three quarters in her pocket. How much money does she have? ______¢

6. Bobby has seven quarters. Cindy has three half-dollars. Who has more money? __________

7-3

Name ____________________

Reteach

2NS5.0

Count Coins

Chapter Resources

Find the value of the coins. Count to find the total amount.

_____¢ _____¢ _____¢ _____¢ Total _____¢

Count coins to check that there is enough money to buy the object. Circle *yes* or *no*.

1. 

_____¢ _____¢ _____¢ _____¢ _____¢

yes no

2. 

_____¢ _____¢ _____¢ _____¢ _____¢ _____¢

yes no

3. 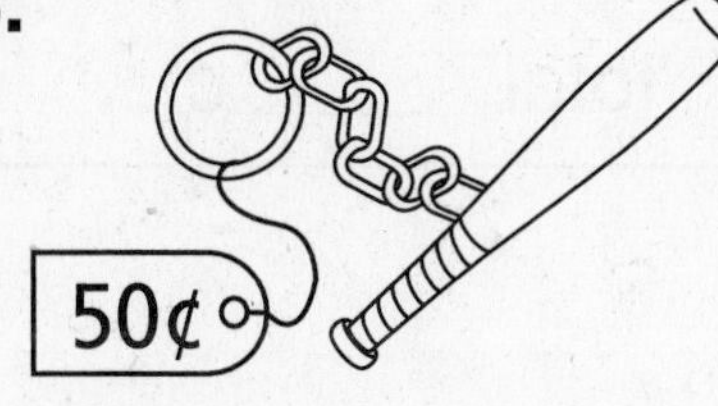

_____¢ _____¢ _____¢ _____¢

yes no

4. 

_____¢ _____¢ _____¢ _____¢ _____¢ _____¢

yes no

Name ______________________________

7-3

Skills Practice

2NS5.0

Count Coins

Count to find the total amount.

1.    

_____¢ _____¢ _____¢ _____¢ _____¢

total _____¢

2.   

_____¢ _____¢ _____¢ _____¢ _____¢

total _____¢

3.       

_____¢ _____¢ _____¢ _____¢ _____¢ _____¢

total _____¢

4.         

_____¢ _____¢ _____¢ _____¢ _____¢ _____¢ _____¢ _____¢ _____¢

total ______¢

Solve.

5. Chuck has two quarters and three nickels in his pocket. How much money does he have? ______¢

6. Carrie has two quarters, a dime, and a penny. How much money does she have? ______¢

Name ________________________________

7-4

Reteach (1)

2NS5.0, 2AF1.2

Problem-Solving Strategy: Act It Out

Chapter Resources

Preparation: Play money is needed for this activity.

Tara has four turtles.
Each turtle cost 10 cents.
How much did Tara spend on turtles?

Step 1
Understand

What do I know?

Tara has four turtles.
Turtles cost 10 cents each.

What do I need to find out?

How much do four turtles cost?

Step 2
Plan

How will I find out?

I can act it out to find out how much four turtles cost.

Step 3
Solve

Act it out.

Put a dime on each turtle. Then skip count the dimes.

4 dimes

_____ dimes = _____ cents

Step 4
Check

Look back.

Does my answer make sense?

_____

Name ______________________________

7-4

Reteach (2)

2NS5.0, 2AF1.2

Problem-Solving Strategy: Act It Out

Preparation: Play money is needed for this activity.

Use coins to act out and solve the problem.

1. Leon has five hermit crabs. Each costs 15 cents. How much money did Leon spend on hermit crabs?

   ______ cents

2. Pat has 13 cents. Her dad gives her 9 cents. How much money does she have in all?

   ______ cents

3. Alisa makes 7 clay pots. She sells them for 12 cents each. How much money does Alisa make?

   ______ cents

4. Art wins 13 games of checkers. He makes 7 cents for charity each time he wins. How much does Art make?

   ______ cents

5. Ellis has 2 dimes, a quarter, and a penny. He wants to buy a fishing rod for 50 cents. Can he buy it?

   ______

6. Ling has 3 quarters, 1 dime, and 4 pennies. What is the most Ling can spend on a snack?

   ______ cents

Name ______________________________

7-4

Skills Practice

2NS5.0, 2AF1.2

Problem-Solving Strategy: Act It Out

Chapter Resources

Preparation: Play money is needed for this activity.

Use coins to act out and solve the problems.

1. Andrea has 52 cents. Her brother gives her a quarter more. How much money does Andrea have?

   ______ cents

2. Reese has 50 cents. Gary has 82 cents. How much more money does Gary have?

   ______ cents

3. Julio finds 17 cents. Luke finds 24 cents. How much more money does Luke find?

   ______ cents

4. Greg has a half dollar in his pocket. His sister gives him a quarter and a penny. How much money does Greg have now?

   ______ cents

5. Miko has 7 pennies, 3 nickels, 1 dime, and 1 quarter. Does she have enough to buy a pen for 50 cents?

   ______

6. Nick has 85 cents. He buys a juice box for 2 dimes. How much does he have now?

   ______ cents

Name ________________________________

7-5

Reteach

2NS5.1, 2NS4.0

Dollar

You can use different coins to make one dollar.

100 pennies = $1.00
20 nickels = $1.00
10 dimes = $1.00
4 quarters = $1.00
2 half-dollars = $1.00
1 dollar bill = $1.00

A dollar is equal to 100¢.  $1.00 = 100¢

Circle the coins in each row that equal $1.00.

1.      

2.           

3.   

4.      

Name ______________________________

7-5

Skills Practice

2NS4.0, 2NS5.2

Dollar

Count the coins. Write the value.
Circle the coins that make one dollar.

1.      ______¢

2.         ______¢

3.           ______¢

4.           ______¢

Solve.

5. It costs one dollar to ride the merry-go-round. Anna has two quarters, two dimes, five nickels, and five pennies. Does she have enough money? ______

6. Leon has three quarters, one dime, one nickel, and two pennies. A loaf of bread costs one dollar. Does Leon have enough to buy a loaf? ______

7. Sylva has four quarters, a penny, and a nickel. If she buys a puzzle for one dollar, how much will Sylva have left?

______¢

7-6

Name ______________________________

Reteach

2NS4.0

Dollars and Cents

You can use decimals and dollar signs to show dollars and cents.

$1.00, $1.25, $1.50, $1.60, $1.70, $1.75, $1.76

Total $1.76 = 176¢

dollars ← → cents

Circle the bills and coins to match the amount in the bank.

1.

2.

3.

Name ______________________________

7-6

Skills Practice

2NS4.0, 2NS5.2

Dollars and Cents

Count the money. Write the amount in dollars and cents.

1.

$ _____._____
dollars cents

2.

$ _____._____
dollars cents

3.

$ _____._____
dollars cents

4.

$ _____._____
dollars cents

Solve.

5. Tyler has two dollar bills, a half dollar, three quarters, and two nickels. How much money can he spend?

$ _____._____

6. Marie has three dollar bills, four quarters, eight dimes, and four pennies. How much money can she spend?

$ _____._____

Name ___

7-7

Reteach

Compare Money Amounts

Count the money you have and compare it to the price.

Yogurt costs $1.25. Is there enough money to buy yogurt?

	+10	+10	+5	+1
$1.00	$1.10	$1.20	$1.25	$1.26

$1.26 is more than $1.25, so you have enough money.

Count the money. Circle the one that is more—the money or the price tag.

1. 

2.        

3. 

4.       

Name ______________________________

7-7

Skills Practice

2NS5.1

Compare Money Amounts

Count. Is there enough money to buy each item? Circle *yes* or *no*.

1. 

yes no

2. 

yes no

3. 

yes no

4. 

yes no

Solve. Use coins and dollar bills to help.

5. Nari wants to buy a book. It costs $4.45. She has four dollar bills, a quarter, a dime, and a nickel. Does she have enough money? ______

6. Estimate the difference between the costs of the plane and the boat. About ________ – about ________ = about ________.

Name ____________________

7-8

Reteach

2NS2.0, 2NS5.0

Add Money

Chapter Resources

Adding money is like adding numbers.

35¢	35		$0.20	20
+ 45¢	+ 45		+ $0.42	+ 42
80¢	80		$0.62	62

Remember to write ¢ or $ and a decimal point in your answer.

Add the money. Circle the answer.

1.      

87¢ 77¢

---

2.    

$0.70 $0.80

---

3.    

$0.75 $0.65

---

4.      

38¢ 83¢

7-8

Name ______________________________

Skills Practice

Add Money

Add.

1. 32¢ + 34¢

2. 14¢ + 62¢

3. 22¢ + 49¢

4. \$0.12 + 0.37

5. \$0.33 + 0.49

6. \$0.32 + 0.65

Solve.

7. Leroy bought a movie ticket for \$0.75. He also bought a magazine for \$0.15. Add to find out how much money he spent. Draw the coins for each amount.

____

Price of a Movie Ticket	Price of a Magazine	Total
\$0.75	\$0.15	\$ ___.___

8. Lee has \$0.61 in her pocket. Her dad gives her \$0.07. How much money does she have now? ________

9. Mr. Adler found 73¢. He had 9¢ in his pocket. How much money does he have? ______

Name ____________________

7-9

Reteach

2NS2.0, 2NS5.0

Subtract Money

Chapter Resources

Subtracting money is like subtracting numbers.

45¢	45	$0.42	42
− 35¢	− 35	− $0.20	− 20
10¢	10	$0.22	22

Remember to write ¢ or $ and a decimal point in your answer.

Subtract the money. Circle the answer.

1. 24¢ − 14¢

8¢ 10¢

2. 66¢ − 28¢

38¢ 28¢

3. 74¢ − 32¢

42¢ 46¢

4. 91¢ − 11¢

70¢ 80¢

5. 89¢ − 41¢

48¢ 50¢

6. $0.49 − $0.22

$0.27 $0.11

7. $0.77 − $0.69

$0.08 $0.02

8. $0.96 − $0.77

$0.19 $0.24

9. $0.51 − $0.07

$0.47 $0.44

10. $0.83 − $0.17

$0.69 $0.66

Name ________________________________

7-9

Skills Practice

2NS2.0, 2NS5.0

Subtract Money

Subtract.

1. 63¢ − 41¢ = ____

2. 64¢ − 12¢ = ____

3. 94¢ − 37¢ = ____

4. $0.87 − $0.32 = ____

5. $0.77 − $0.41 = ____

6. $0.28 − $0.26 = ____

Solve.

7. Luke had $0.75. He spent $0.32. Subtract to find out how much money he has now. Draw the coins. ________

How Much Luke Has	How Much Money Luke Spent	What He Has Left
$0.75	$0.32	$.

8. Logan had $0.79 in his pocket. He spent $0.17. How much money does he have left?

____

9. Mrs. Paul gave 65¢ to her son. He spent 32¢. How much money does he have left? ______

Name ______________________________

7-10

Reteach (1)

2NS5.0, 2MR1.1

Problem-Solving Investigation: Choose a Strategy

Joe's dad bought 20 bananas.
They ate six the first day.
How many bananas do they have left?

Step 1 **Understand**	**What do I know?** Joe's dad bought 20 bananas. They ate six bananas. **What do I need to find out?** How many bananas do they have left?
Step 2 **Plan**	**How will I find out?** I can draw a picture to find out how many bananas they have left. But subtracting would be faster. I can subtract to find out how many bananas they have left.
Step 3 **Solve**	**Write a number sentence.** 20 ◯ 6 = ______ bananas Joe has ______ bananas left.
Step 4 **Check**	**Look back.** Why did I need to subtract instead of add? Did I choose the right strategy?

Name ____________________

7-10

Reteach (2)

2NS5.0, 2MR1.1

Problem-Solving Investigation: Choose a Strategy

Choose a strategy and solve.

1. Taylor has 14 kittens. Rhonda has 10 kittens. How many kittens do they have?

14 ◯ 10 = ______ kittens

They have ______ kittens.

2. Lauren has 24 carrots. Her pet rabbit eats 13. How many carrots does she have now?

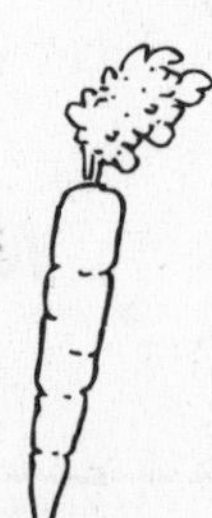

24 ◯ 13 = ______ carrots

Lauren has ______ carrots left.

3. Gloria has $1.07. Vic has $1.01. About how much do they have?

They have about $ ___.____

4. Mike has $0.41. Kyle has $0.59. How much money do they have?

They have $ ___.____

5. Karen has 50 comic books. She gives 35 to Dale. How many comic books does she have left?

She has ______ comic books left.

6. Maria has four markers. Kyle has 12 markers. How many more markers does Kyle have?

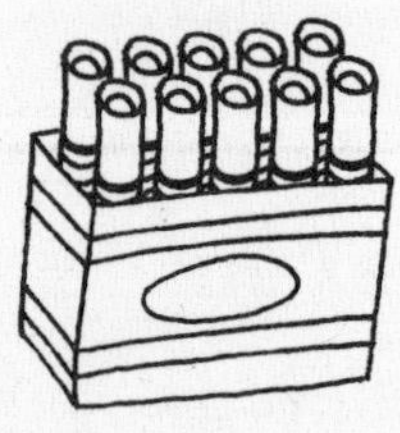

Kyle has ______ more markers than Maria.

7-10

Name ______________________

Skills Practice

2NS5.0, 2MR1.1

Problem-Solving Investigation: Choose a Strategy

Choose a strategy and solve.

Problem-Solving Strategy
- Act It Out
- Choose an Operation
- Guess and Check
- Draw a Picture

1. Mr. Gary gave his son a quarter. He gave 50¢ to his daughter. How much money did he give his children? _____

2. Amy has two dollars, a quarter, and four nickels. Tony has three dollars, a half-dollar, a dime, and eight pennies. How much do they have altogether? Is your answer reasonable?

_______ _______

3. There are 13 dimes on the table. Five more dimes are in the jar. How many dimes are there in all? ____________

4. Jen gets $1.50 a week for allowance. If she saves her money for four weeks, how much money would she have? _______

5. Ted has a dollar and two quarters in his pocket. His friend gives him a half-dollar and a nickel. His teacher gives him two cents. How much money does Ted have now? _______

6. Alex bought an apple for $0.55 and a banana for $0.75. Estimate how much money Alex spent. about _______

Name ______________________________

8-1

Reteach

2NS3.1, 2MR1.2

Equal Groups

Chapter Resources

Preparation: Counters are needed for this activity.

Use ⬤ to keep track of equal groups.

Place a ⬤ on each equal group. Then count to see how many equal groups.

_____ equal groups

Use ⬤ to see how many equal groups.

1. 

_____ equal groups

2.  _____ equal groups

3. 

 _____ equal groups

4.    

_____ equal groups

8-1

Name ______________________________

Skills Practice

2NS3.1, 2MR1.2

Equal Groups

Preparation: Counters are needed for this activity.

Skip count. Write how many in all.

1. 

 ___4___ ___8___ ______ ______ in all

2. ☆☆☆ ☆☆☆ ☆☆☆ ☆☆☆

 ______ ______ ______ ______ in all

3. 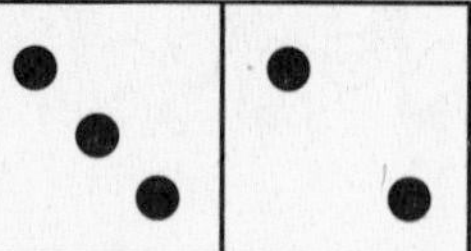 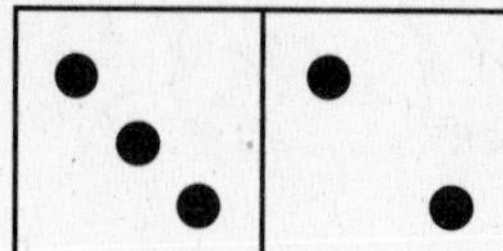 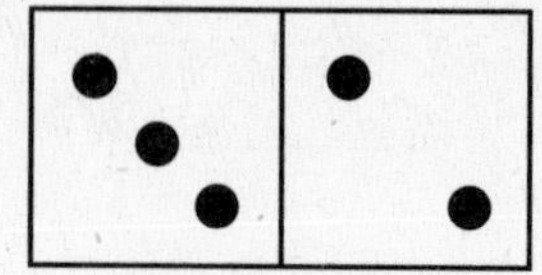

 ______ ______ ______ ______ in all

Use counters to solve.

4. Mollie uses counters to find how many equal groups there are in problem 1. How many counters will she use?

 ______ counters

5. Jamal has 3 groups of marbles. Each group has 4 marbles. Use counters to model Jamal's groups. Skip count to find how many there are in all.

 ______ marbles

Name ______________________

8-2

Reteach

Repeated Addition

2NS3.1, 2MR1.2

Chapter Resources

Preparation: Counters are needed for this activity.

Put a ◯ on each group. Count the ◯.
Count how many cubes are under each counter.

1. 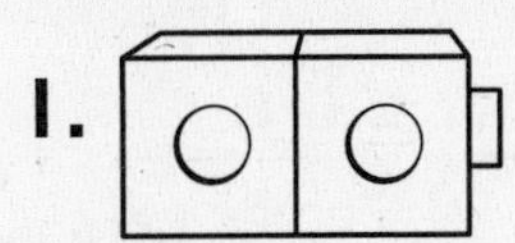 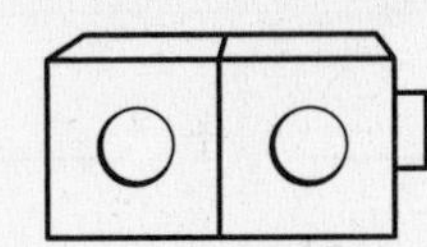 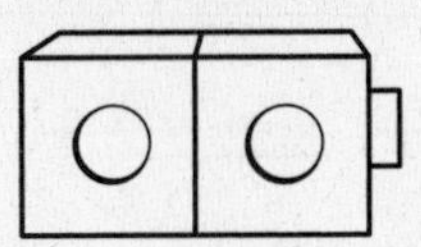 __3__ counters

Add 2 for every counter. Write the numbers and the sum.

__2__ + __2__ + __2__ = __6__ cubes

3 groups of 2 = __6__ cubes

__3__ × __2__ = __6__ cubes

2. 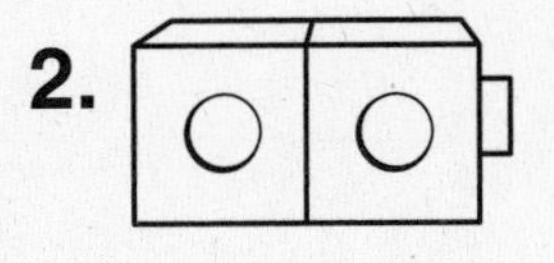 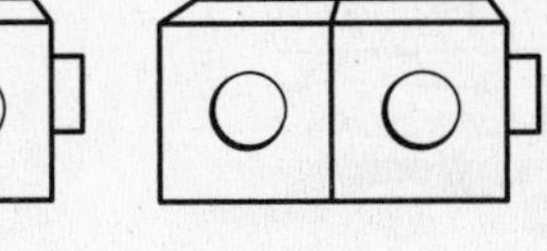 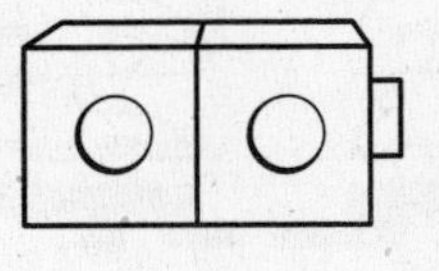 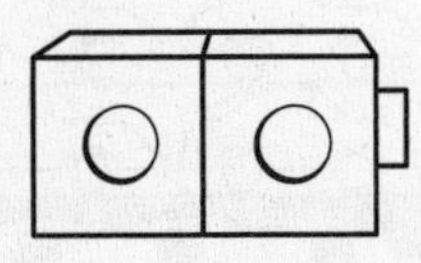

◯ + ◯ + ◯ + ◯ = ____

____ groups of ____ = ____ cubes

____ × ____ = ____

3. 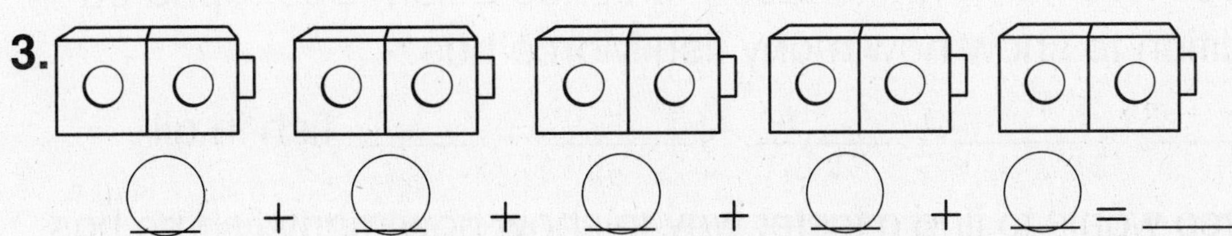

◯ + ◯ + ◯ + ◯ + ◯ = ____

____ groups of ____ = ____ cubes

____ × ____ = ____

Name ______________________________

8-2

Skills Practice

2NS3.1, 2MR3.0

Repeated Addition

Add. Then multiply.

1.

__2__ + __2__ + ____ + ____ + ____ = ____

____ × ____ = ____

2.

____ + ____ + ____ = ____

____ × ____ = ____

3.

____ + ____ = ____

____ × ____ = ____

Solve.

4. Marco has 4 fish tanks. Each tank has 2 fish. Use repeated addition to show how many fish Marco has.

____ + ____ + ____ + ____ = ____ fish in all

5. Marco wants to find a faster way to show how many fish he has. Write a multiplication sentence to show him.

____ × ____ = ____ fish in all

Name ______________________________

8-3

Reteach

2NS3.1, 2MR1.2

Arrays

Chapter Resources

Color each row a different color. Count how many rows. Count how many in each row.

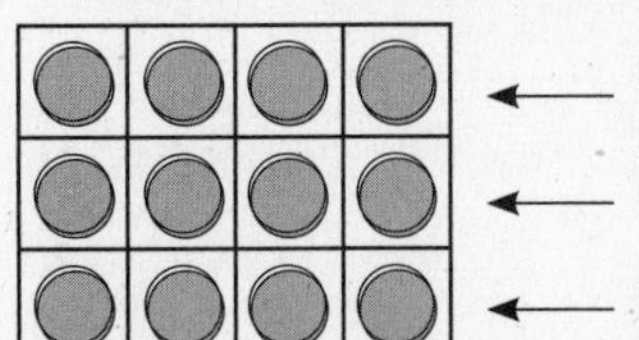

_____ × _____ = _____
rows in each row in all

Color to count. Write a multiplication sentence for your count.

1. 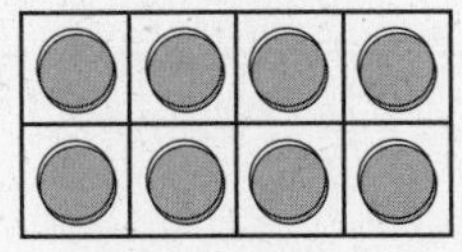

_____ × _____ = _____
rows in each row in all

_____ × _____ = _____

2. 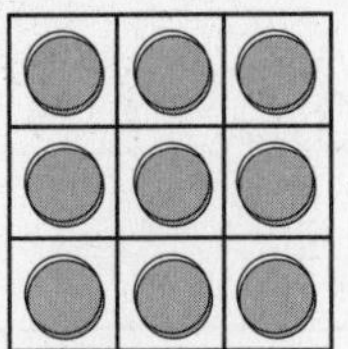

_____ × _____ = _____
rows in each row in all

_____ × _____ = _____

3. 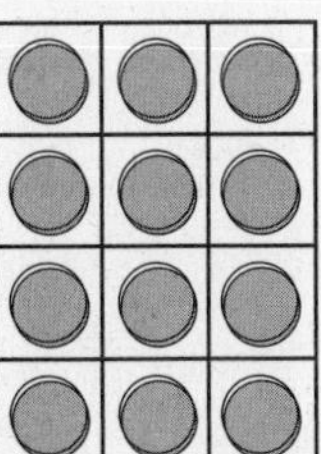

_____ × _____ = _____
rows in each row in all

_____ × _____ = _____

4. 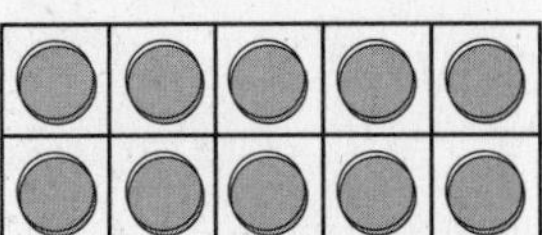

_____ × _____ = _____
rows in each row in all

_____ × _____ = _____

Name ______________________

8-3

Skills Practice

2NS3.1, 2MR1.2

Arrays

Color the array. Find the product.

1. 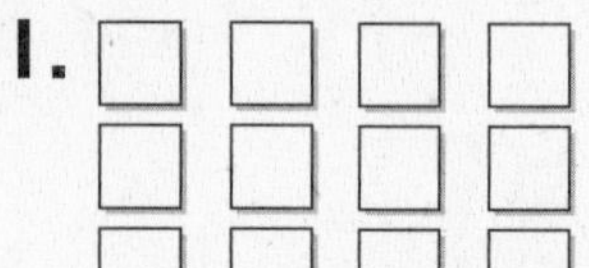

3 × 4 = 12
rows   in each row   in all

2. 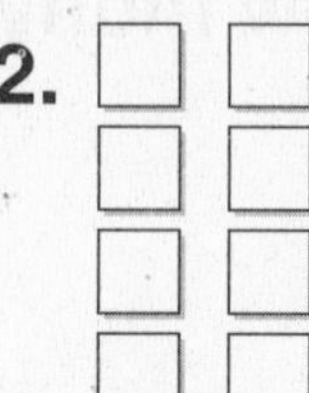

_____ × _____ = _____
rows   in each row   in all

Multiply.

3. 4 × 3 = _____

4. 6 × 2 = _____

5. 4 × 5 = _____

6. 3 × 3 = _____

7. 5 × 3 = _____

8. 6 × 3 = _____

Solve. Draw a picture if you need help.

9. Tomás has a carton of eggs. There are 2 rows in the carton. Each row has 6 eggs. How many eggs does Tomás have?

_____ rows × _____ in each row = _____ eggs in all

10. Elsa is baking muffins. Her muffin tin has 4 rows. She can bake 3 muffins in each row. How many muffins can Elsa bake in all?

_____ rows × _____ in each row = _____ muffins in all

Name ______

8-4

Reteach

2NS3.3, 2MR3.0

Multiply 2s and 5s

Chapter Resources

Preparation: A set of counters is needed for this activity.

Using a doubles fact is the same as multiplying by 2.
You can use counters to help.

Put a counter on each addend. Write the number of counters in the ◯. Multiply.

 + 3 = ◯ × 3 = ______

Put a counter on each addend. Write the number of counters. Multiply.

1. 2 + 2 = ◯ × 2 =

2. 4 + 4 = ◯ × 4 =

3. 5 + 5 = ◯ × 5 =

4. 6 + 6 = ◯ × 6 =

5. 7 + 7 = ◯ × 7 =

6. 8 + 8 = ◯ × 8 =

Name ______________________

8-4

Skills Practice

2NS3.3

Multiply 2s and 5s

Multiply.

1. $2 \times 4 =$ 8

2. $5 \times 0 =$ ______

3. $5 \times 2 =$ ______

4. $1 \times 5 =$ ______

5. $2 \times 6 =$ ______

6. $5 \times 3 =$ ______

7. $7 \times 2 =$ ______

8. $4 \times 5 =$ ______

9. $2 \times 8 =$ ______

10. $5 \times 6 =$ ______

11. $9 \times 2 =$ ______

12. $7 \times 5 =$ ______

Multiply to solve.

13. Sophie has 5 colors of yarn. She has 3 balls of each color. How many total balls of yarn does Sophie have?

______ × ______ = ______ balls of yarn

14. Miguel has 2 bags of buttons. Each bag has 8 buttons. How many buttons does Miguel have?

______ × ______ = ______ buttons

15. Sam collects baseball cards of 5 teams. He has 4 cards from each team. How many baseball cards does Sam have in all?

______ × ______ = ______ baseball cards

Name ____________________

8-5

Reteach (1)

2NS3.0, 2MR1.0

Problem-Solving Strategy: Draw a Picture

Chapter Resources

Sanders' Orchard sells bags of apples. Each bag has 4 apples. Mary buys 16 apples in all. How many bags does she buy?

Step 1 **Understand**

What do I know?

Each bag has 4 apples.
Mary buys a total of 16 apples.

What do I need to find out?

How many bags does Mary buy?

Step 2 **Plan**

How will I find out?

I will draw a picture of each of Mary's apples.
I will circle groups of 4.

Step 3 **Solve**

Draw a picture.

 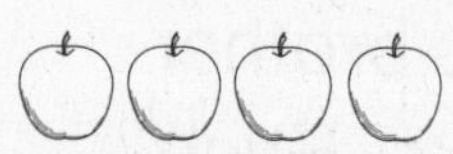

How many groups are there? __4__ groups

So, Mary buys __4__ bags of apples.

Step 4 **Check**

Look back.

Does my answer make sense? __yes__

Name ______________________________

8-5

Reteach (2)

2NS3.0, 2MR1.0

Problem-Solving Strategy: Draw a Picture

Draw a picture to solve. **Show your work here.**

1. A.J., Vic, and Maria share a sack of pears. There are 12 pears in the sack. How many pears does each friend get?

______ pears each

2. Jack's dad gives Jack 18 blocks. The blocks come in sets of 6. How many sets does Jack's dad give?

______ sets of blocks

3. Ida knits 15 hats. She puts the hats into 3 gift boxes. Each box has the same number of hats. How many hats are in each box?

______ hats.

4. Mateo and his brother share 14 books. Each brother puts the same number of books on his own shelf. How many books does each brother get?

______ books

Name ______________________________

8-5

Skills Practice

2NS3.0, 2MR1.0

Problem-Solving Strategy: Draw a Picture

Draw a picture to solve. **Show your work here.**

1. Grandpa Nathan wants to ship 20 crates. Each truck can hold 4 crates. How many trucks does Grandpa Nathan need?

   ______ trucks

2. Leona is packing 24 plates. If she puts 4 plates in a box, how many boxes will Leona need?

   ______ boxes

3. Ivan bought 12 balloons. He gave the balloons to 4 of his cousins. How many balloons did each cousin get?

   ______ balloons

4. Ms. Kim gave 15 paint pots to her art class. She has 5 students. How many paint pots did each student get?

   ______ paint pots

Name ______________________________

8-6

Reteach

2NS3.3

Multiply 10s

Chapter Resources

Preparation: Base-ten blocks are needed for this activity.

Use  to help multiply by 10.
Count the number of tens rods. Then, count by 10 to see how many single blocks.

1 2 3 4 **There are 4 tens rods.**

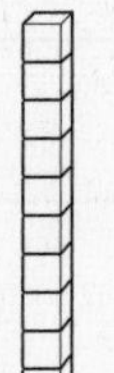
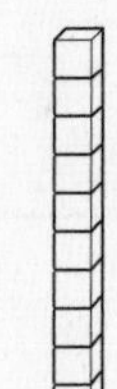
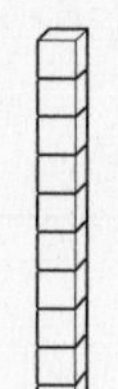
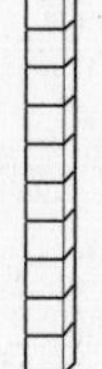

10 20 30 40 **There are 40 single blocks.**

4 rods × 10 blocks in rod = 40 blocks in all

Use 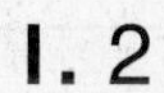 to multiply.

1. 2 × 10 = ______

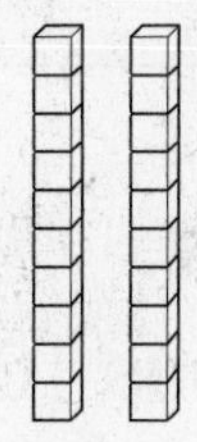

6 × 10 = ______

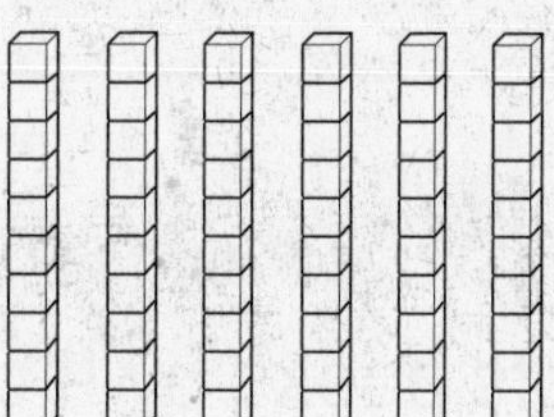

2. 5 × 10 = ______

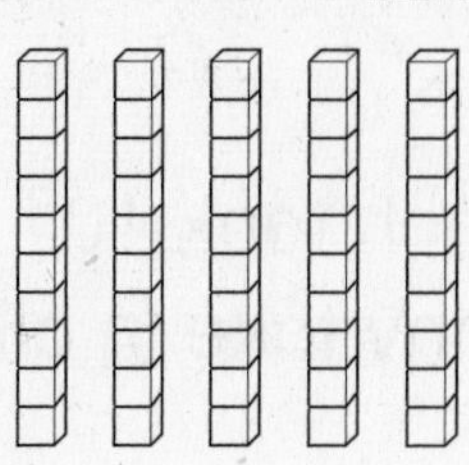

3 × 10 = ______

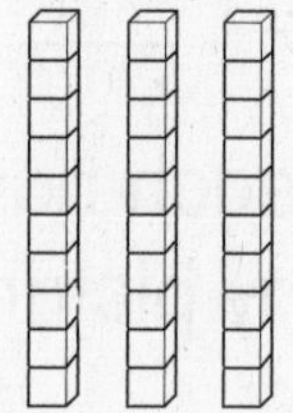

Name ______________________________

8-6

Skills Practice

2NS3.3

Multiply 10s

Multiply.

1. 2 × 10 = ______ **2.** 9 × 10 = ______ **3.** 3 × 10 = ______

4. 8 × 10 = ______ **5.** 5 × 10 = ______ **6.** 6 × 10 = ______

7. 1 × 10 = ______ **8.** 4 × 10 = ______ **9.** 10 × 7 = ______

10. 10 × 4 = ______ **11.** 10 × 2 = ______ **12.** 10 × 10 = ______

13. 10 × 8 = ______ **14.** 10 × 3 = ______ **15.** 10 × 5 = ______

Multiply to solve.

17. Rae collects books by 4 different authors. So far, she has 10 books by each author. How many books does Rae have in her collection?

______ × ______ = ______ books

18. Julie and Johnny each have a camera. They each took 10 pictures. How many pictures did Julie and Johnny take in all?

______ × ______ = ______ pictures

Name ______________________________

8-7

Reteach

2NS3.2, 2MR1.2

Repeated Subtraction and Division

Chapter Resources

You can draw a picture to help.

There are 12 bananas.
There are 4 bananas in a bunch.
How many bunches are there?

Draw dots to show the first number.

Cross out groups of the second number.
Count how many Xs to solve.

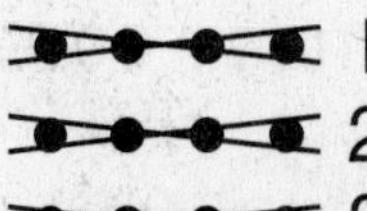

There are __3__ bunches.

Solve. Draw a picture to help. **Show Your Work**

1. 20 people are on teams.
There are 5 people on each team.

How many teams can you have?

______ teams

2. 15 students share rides to school.
There are 3 students in each car.

How many cars do they take?

______ cars

3. Tim's grandpa is here for 28 days.
There are 7 days in each week.

How many weeks is Tim's grandpa here?

______ weeks

Name ______________________________

8-7

Skills Practice

2NS3.2, 2MR1.2

Repeated Subtraction and Division

Preparation: A set of connecting cubes is needed for this activity.

Use cubes. Make equal groups.
Subtract. Then divide.

1\. 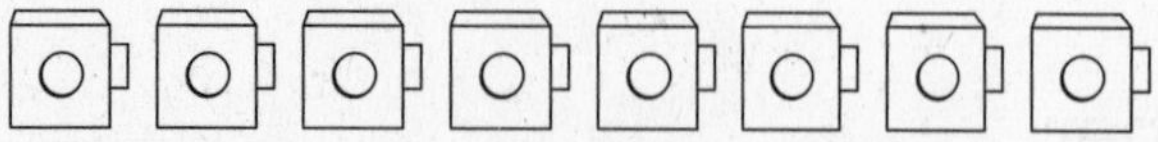 Subtract groups of 2.
How many equal groups can you make?

You get _____ groups of 2.

_____ ÷ _____ = _____

2\. 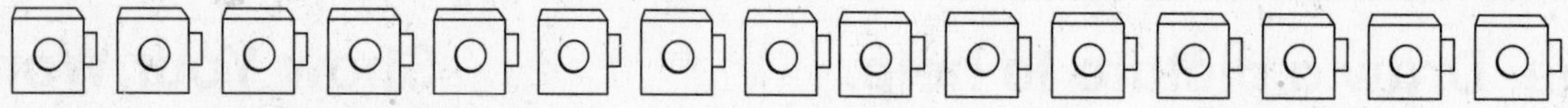 Subtract groups of 5.
How many equal groups can you make?

You get _____ groups of 5.

_____ ÷ _____ = _____

Use cubes to solve.

3\. Sally has 16 blocks. She puts them into groups of 2. How many equal groups of 2 does Sally have?

_____ ÷ _____ = _____

4\. Tanya has 20 beads. She puts them into groups of 4. How many equal groups of 4 does Tanya have?

_____ ÷ _____ = _____

Name ____________________

8-8

Reteach

2NS3.2, 2MR1.2

Find Equal Shares

Chapter Resources

Preparation: Crayons are needed for this activity.

Color to make equal groups.

Make each group a new color.

6 ○

3 equal groups

__2__ in each group

__6__ ÷ __3__ = ______

Color to make equal groups. Write how many in each group. Divide.

1. 10 ○

5 equal groups

______ in each group

______ ÷ ______ = ______

2. 14 ○

2 equal groups

______ in each group

______ ÷ ______ = ______

3. 8 ○

4 equal groups

______ in each group

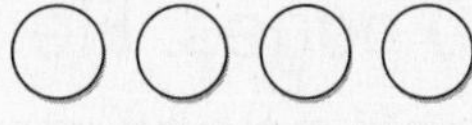

______ ÷ ______ = ______

Name ______________________________

8-8

Skills Practice

2NS3.2, 2MR1.2

Find Equal Shares

Use counters to make equal shares. How many are in each group? Divide.

1. 6 counters 2 equal groups _____ ÷ _____ = _____	**2.** 18 counters 9 equal groups _____ ÷ _____ = _____
3. 20 counters 4 equal groups _____ ÷ _____ = _____	**4.** 12 counters 4 equal groups _____ ÷ _____ = _____
5. 15 counters 5 equal groups _____ ÷ _____ = _____	**6.** 16 counters 2 equal groups _____ ÷ _____ = _____
7. 18 counters 6 equal groups _____ ÷ _____ = _____	**8.** 25 counters 5 equal groups _____ ÷ _____ = _____

Solve.

9. Leslie has 24 peaches. She put equal groups of peaches into 3 bowls. How many peaches are in each bowl?

24 ÷ 3 = _____ peaches

10. Mr. Chan wrote 20 pages. He divided the pages into 4 equal chapters. How many pages are in each chapter?

20 ÷ 4 = _____ pages

Name ____________________

8-9

Reteach (1)

2NS3.0, 2MR1.1

Problem-Solving Investigation: Choose a Strategy

Chapter Resources

Gabe has 3 shelves.
Each shelf has 7 books.
How many total books does Gabe have?

Step 1 Read	**What do I know?** There are 3 shelves. There are 7 books on each shelf. **What do I need to find out?** How many books in all.
Step 2 Plan	**How will I find out?** I can draw a picture. With a picture, I can actually see how many books.
Step 3 Solve	**Draw a picture.** Gabe has 21 books.
Step 4 Check	**Look back.** Did I draw a picture showing 3 shelves with 7 books? yes Does my answer show how many total books? yes

8-9

Name ______________________________

Reteach (2)

2NS3.0, 2MR1.1

Problem-Solving Investigation: Choose a Strategy

Choose a strategy. Solve.

Problem-Solving Strategies
Make a table
Use a model
Draw a picture

Show your work here.

1. Evan is sending boxes of old books to his pen pal. He can fit 5 books in a box.

   If Evan sends 3 boxes, how many books can he pack?

   _____ books

2. The Garcia family has 6 flashlights. Each flashlight needs 2 batteries.

   How many batteries do they need to buy?

   _____ batteries

3. The five Li sisters share 25 barrettes. They have an equal number of barrettes.

   How many barrettes does each sister have?

   _____ barrettes each

Name ______________________________

8-9

Skills Practice

2NS3.0, 2MR1.1

Problem-Solving Investigation: Choose a Strategy

Choose a strategy. Solve.

Problem-Solving Strategies
Make a table
Use a model
Draw a picture

1. Seven cousins share 14 friendship bracelets. They each have the same number of bracelets.

   How many bracelets does each cousin have?

   ______ bracelets each

2. Abby made 12 dollars babysitting. She babysat for 3 hours.

   How many dollars did Abby make each hour?

   ______ dollars each hour

3. Devon feeds his three rabbits 15 carrots. Each rabbit eats the same number of carrots.

   How many carrots does each rabbit eat?

   ______ carrots each

   What if Devon fed the rabbits 18 carrots?

   ______ carrots each

4. Liam made 6 pies. Each pie has 3 apples.

   How many apples did Liam use in all?

   ______ apples

   How many apples would Liam need for 8 pies?

   ______ apples

Name ______________________________

8-10

Reteach

2NS3.2, 2MR1.2

Equal Groups with Remainders

Chapter Resources

Preparation: Crayons are needed for this activity.

Color to make equal groups. Color to find the remainder.

Make each group a new color.

The counters you do not color is the remainder.

7 counters
3 equal groups of 2 counters
1 counter left over

$7 \div 3 =$ 2 remainder 1

Color to make equal groups. Divide. Write the remainder if there is one.

1\. $13 \div 3 =$ ______ remainder ______

2\. $9 \div 2 =$ ______ remainder ______

3\. $17 \div 3 =$ ______ remainder ______

8-10

Name ______________________________

Skills Practice

2NS3.2, 2MR1.2

Equal Groups with Remainders

Preparation: Connecting cubes are needed for this activity.

Use cubes to make equal groups. Divide.
Write the remainder if there is one.

1. 10 marbles are shared by 3 sisters.

   10 ÷ 3 = ______ remainder ______

   Each sister has ______ marbles, and there is ______ left over.

2. 17 toys are shared by 3 dogs.

   17 ÷ 3 = ______ remainder ______

   Each dog gets ______ toys, and there are ______ toys left over.

3. 20 glasses of lemonade are shared by 6 children.

   20 ÷ 6 = ______ remainder ______

   Each child gets ______ glasses, and there are ______ glasses left over.

4. Jin, Cass, and Nelle found 16 strawberries. They shared the strawberries equally. Were there any left over? ______

   16 ÷ 3 = ______ remainder ______

5. Jaime and June shared 12 crackers equally. Were there any left over? ______

   12 ÷ 2 = ______ remainder ______

Name ______

9-1

Reteach

Unit Fractions

2NS4.1

Chapter Resources

Fractions show equal parts of one whole.

2 equal parts

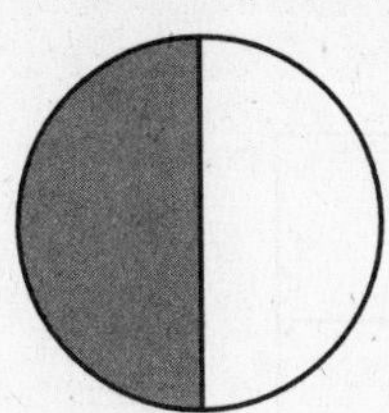

1 of ___ parts is shaded.

$\frac{1}{\_\_}$

3 equal parts

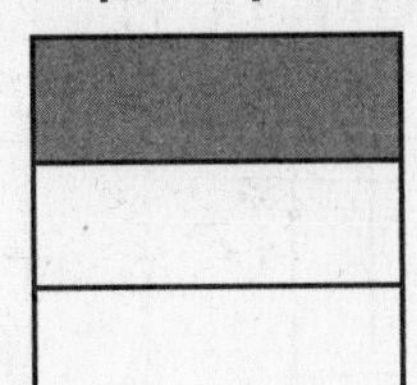

1 of ___ parts is shaded.

$\frac{1}{\_\_}$

4 equal parts

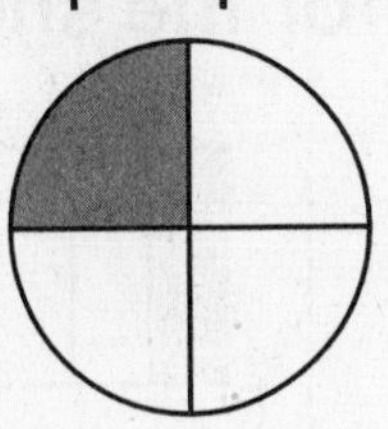

1 of ___ parts is shaded.

$\frac{1}{\_\_}$

8 equal parts

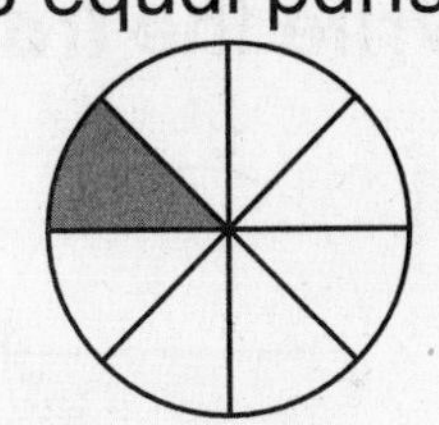

1 of ___ parts is shaded.

$\frac{1}{\_\_}$

Write the fraction for the shaded part.

1. 4 equal parts

1 of ___ parts is shaded.

1

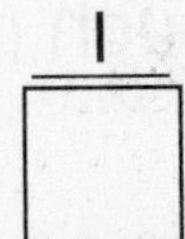

2. 8 equal parts

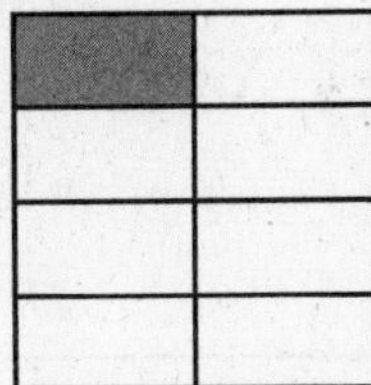

1 of ___ parts is shaded.

1

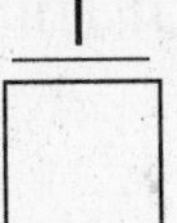

---

3. 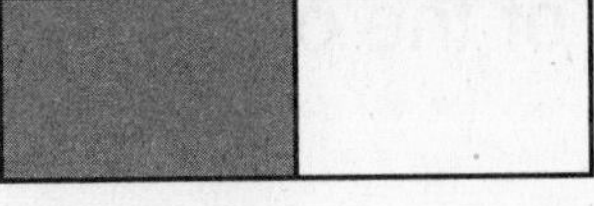

___

4. 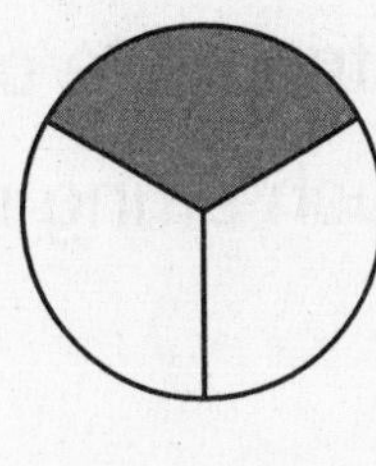

___

5. 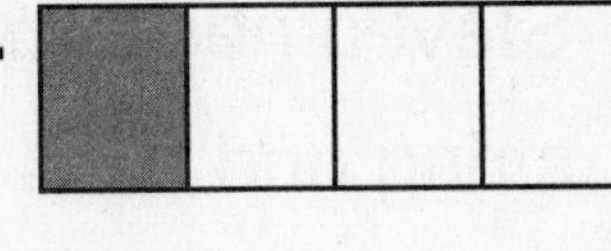

___

Name ______________________________

9-1

Skills Practice

2NS4.1

Unit Fractions

Preparation: Crayons are needed for this activity.

Write the fraction for the shaded part.

1. 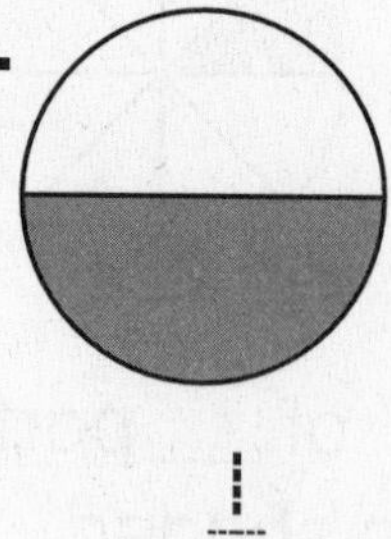

$\frac{1}{2}$

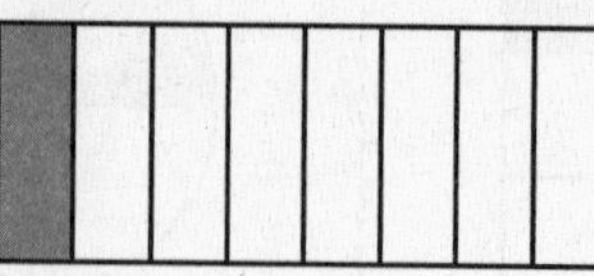

___

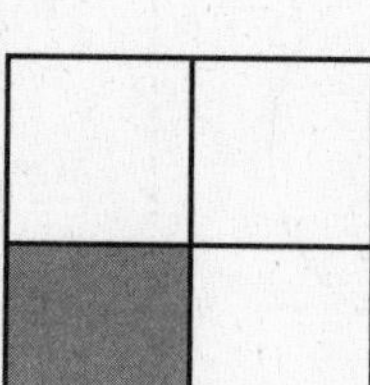

___

Color part of each figure to show the fraction.

2. 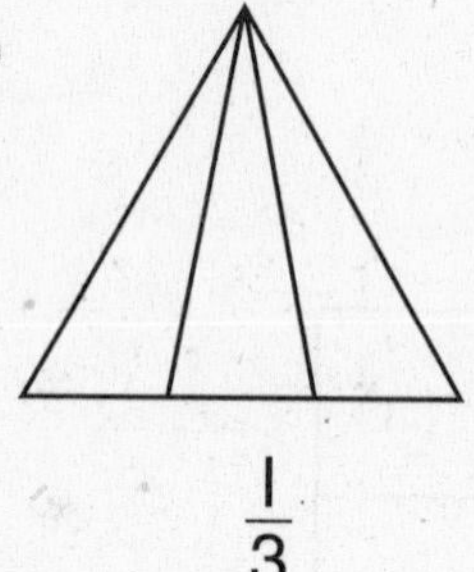

$\frac{1}{3}$

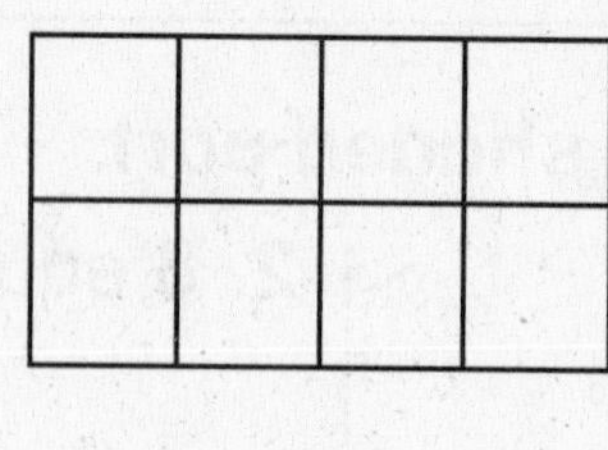

$\frac{1}{8}$

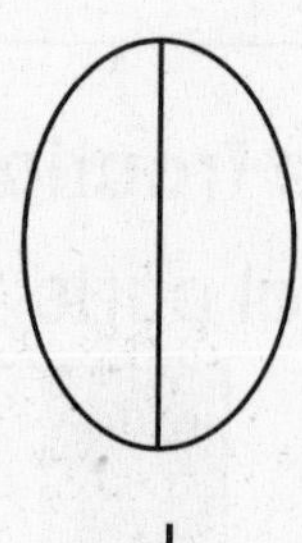

$\frac{1}{2}$

Solve.

3. Lori has a glass of milk. She drinks half of it. How much milk is left?

___

4. Steven needs a piece of string. He cuts off $\frac{3}{4}$ of the piece of string and uses it. How much string is left?

____

Name ______________________________

9-2

Reteach

2NS4.0, 2MR1.2

Other Fractions

Chapter Resources

A fraction can name the number of equal parts that are shaded. Count the number of equal parts that are shaded.

4 equal parts

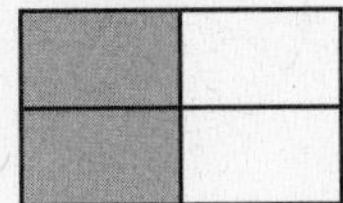

_____ of 4 equal parts are shaded.

$\frac{\quad}{4}$

6 equal parts

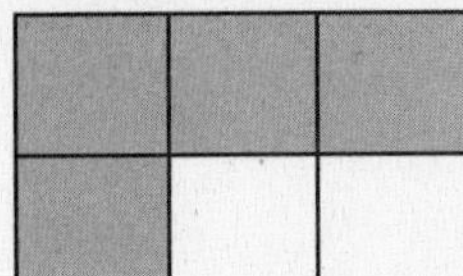

_____ of 6 equal parts are shaded.

$\frac{\quad}{6}$

Write the fraction for the shaded part.

1. 8 equal parts

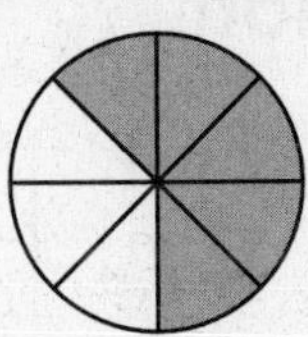

_____ of 8 parts are shaded.

$\frac{\quad}{8}$

2. 3 equal parts

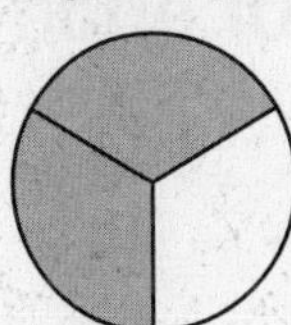

_____ of 3 parts are shaded.

$\frac{\quad}{3}$

3.

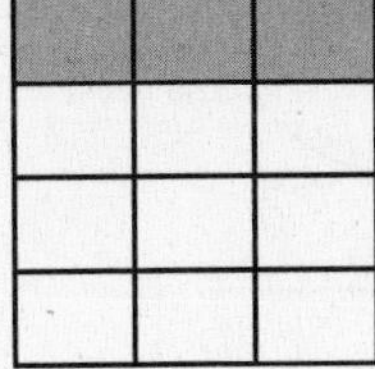

___

4.

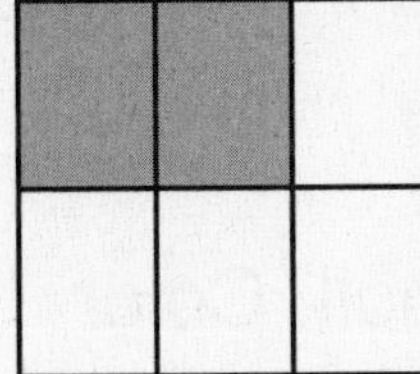

___

5.

___

9-2

Name ______________________________

Skills Practice

2NS4.0, 2MR1.2

Other Fractions

Preparation: Crayons are needed for this activity.

Write the fraction for the shaded part.

1. 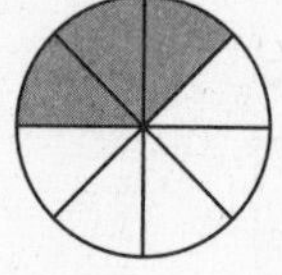

$\frac{3}{8}$

2. 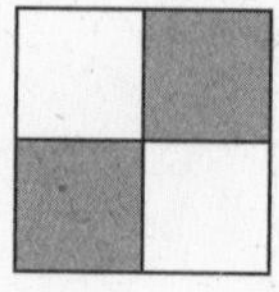

____

3. 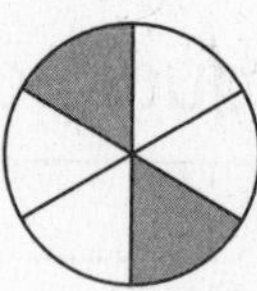

____

4. 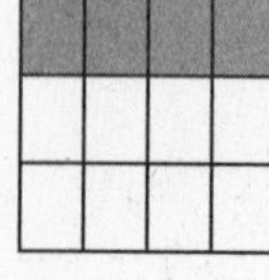

____

5. 

____

6. 

____

Color part of each figure to show the fraction.

7. 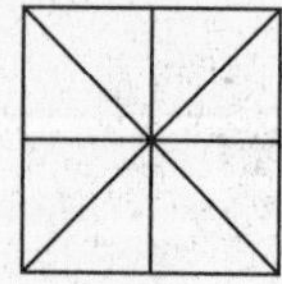

$\frac{5}{8}$

8. 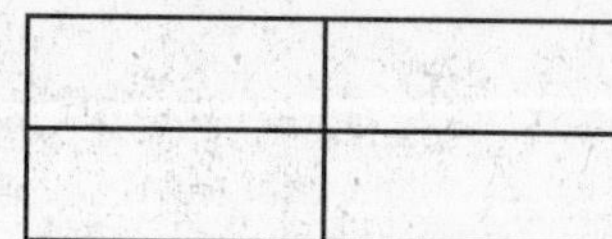

$\frac{3}{4}$

9. 

$\frac{3}{6}$

10. Bill eats some pizza. Color three-fourths of the circle to see how much Bill eats. Write the correct fraction.

____

11. Mr. Li is putting tile in his hall. Color five-eighths of the rectangle to see how much he has done. Write the correct fraction.

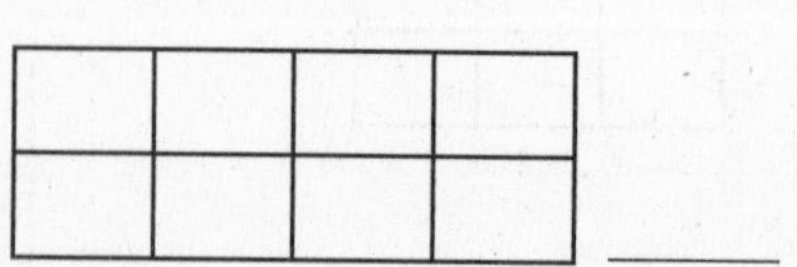

____

Name ____________________

9-3

Reteach (1)

2NS4.0, 2MR1.0

Problem-Solving Strategy: Draw a Picture

Chapter Resources

Nina put frosting on 2 parts of a cake.
The cake has six equal parts.
What fraction of the cake has frosting?

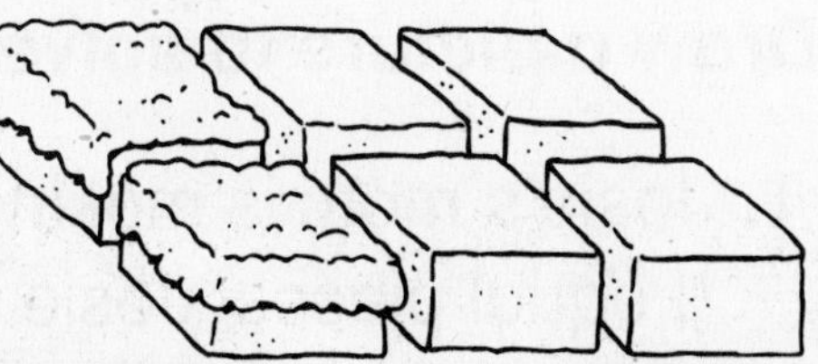

Step 1 **Understand**	**What do I know?** There is frosting on 2 parts of a cake. The cake has six equal parts. **What do I need to find out?** The fraction of the cake that has frosting.
Step 2 **Plan**	**How will I find out?** I can draw a picture. A picture will help me see the fractions.
Step 3 **Solve**	**Draw a picture.** ___ of the cake has frosting.
Step 4 **Check**	**Look back.** How did drawing a picture help me solve the problem?

Name ___________________________________

9-3

Reteach (2)

2NS4.0, 2MR1.0

Problem-Solving Strategy: Draw a Picture

Draw a picture to solve. Show your work.

1. Josie's mom is making a sandwich. She cuts the sandwich into 4 equal pieces. Josie eats 2 pieces. Her mom eats 1 piece. What fraction shows how much of the sandwich they eat?

Josie and her mom eat ___ of the sandwich.

2. Tom is making a spinner for a game. He draws a circle with 6 equal parts. Then, he colors 1 part blue. What fraction of the spinner is *not* blue?

___ of Tom's spinner is not blue.

3. Kim and her dad are making a pizza with 8 equal slices. They put mushrooms on the first 4 slices. Then, they put peppers on the last 4 slices. Kim does not like peppers. What fraction of the pizza can she eat?

Kim can eat ___ of the pizza.

Name ______________________________

9-3

Skills Practice

2NS4.0, 2MR1.0

Problem-Solving Strategy: Draw a Picture

Draw a picture to solve. Show your work.

1. Ben is making a comic strip. First, he draws a rectangle with five equal parts. Then, Ben draws in 3 of the parts. What fraction of the comic strip did Ben draw so far?

Ben has drawn ___ of the comic strip.

2. Jose's grandma is making a quilt. The quilt is a rectangle with 9 equal parts. 4 of the parts are green. What fraction of the quilt is green?

___ of the quilt is green.

3. Tina cuts a pie into 6 equal slices. She puts whipped cream on two of the slices. She leaves the other slices plain. What fraction shows how many slices are plain?

Tina leaves ___ of the slices plain.

Name ______________________

9-4

Reteach

2NS4.2, 2NS4.3

Fractions Equal to 1

Chapter Resources

You can write a fraction for the whole.

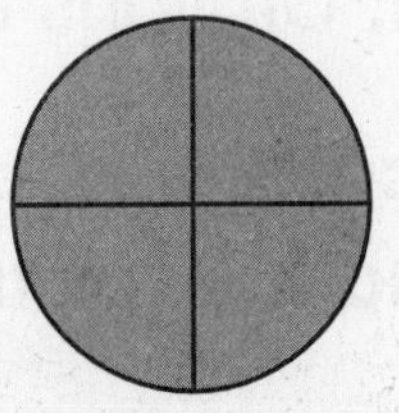

There are 4 shaded parts.
There are 4 equal parts.

The number of shaded parts is the **top** number of this fraction. → $\frac{4}{4}$ ← The total number of equal parts is the **bottom** number of a fraction.

The fraction $\frac{4}{4}$ equals 1.

Count the parts in each whole.
Then write the fraction for the whole.

1. 

____

2. 

____

3. 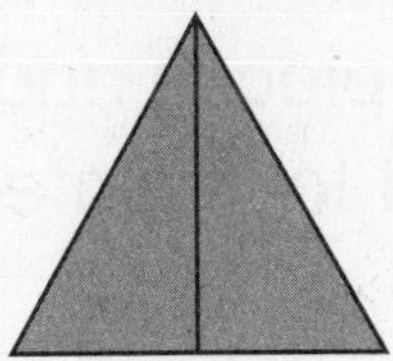

____

4. 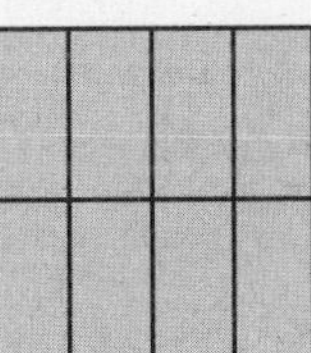

____

5. 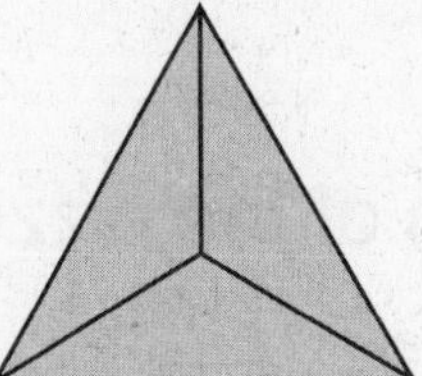

____

6. 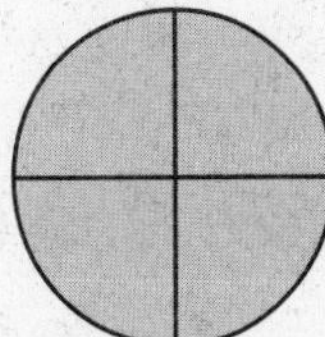

____

Name ______________________________

9-4

Skills Practice

2NS4.2, 2NS4.3

Fractions Equal to 1

Preparation: Crayons are needed for this activity.

Count and color all parts of each whole. Then write the fraction for the whole.

1.

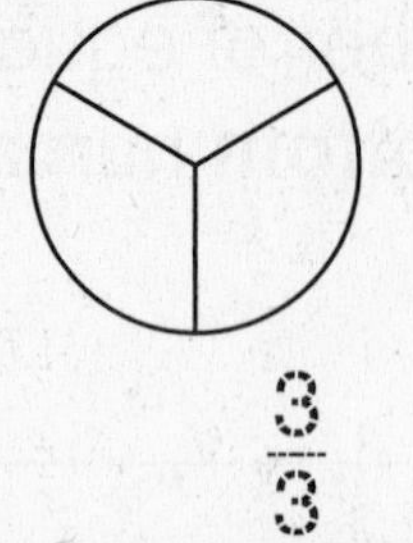

$\frac{3}{3}$

2.

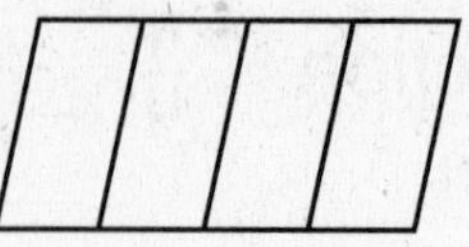

______

3.

______

4.

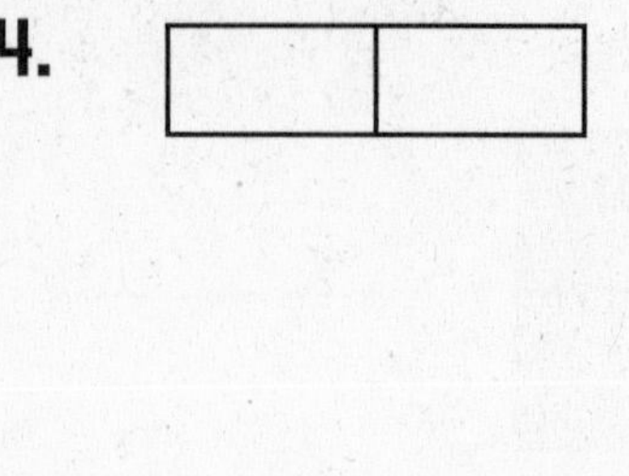

______

5.

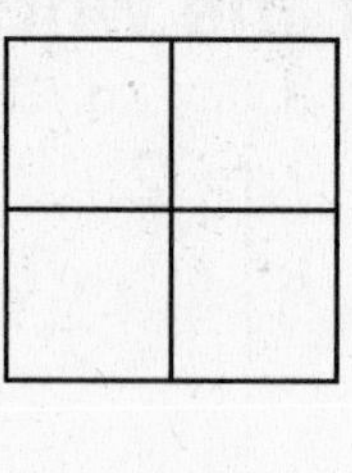

______

6.

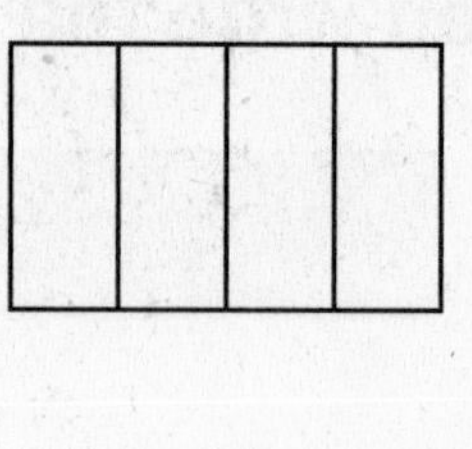

______

7. Dave has a pizza. It has been sliced into 8 equal pieces and none of it has been eaten. Color each piece. Next to it, write the fraction for the pizza.

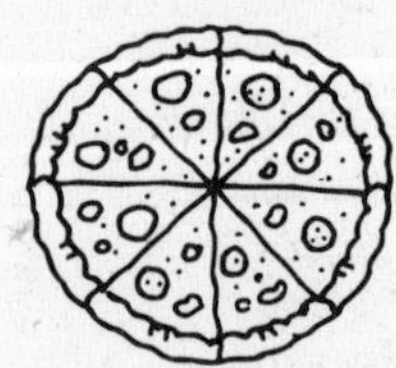

8. Dave eats two slices of his pizza. What fraction of the pizza did he eat?

______

Name ______________________________

9-5

Reteach

2NS4.1, 2MR1.2

Compare Fractions

Chapter Resources

Compare the shaded parts.
Which fraction is greater?

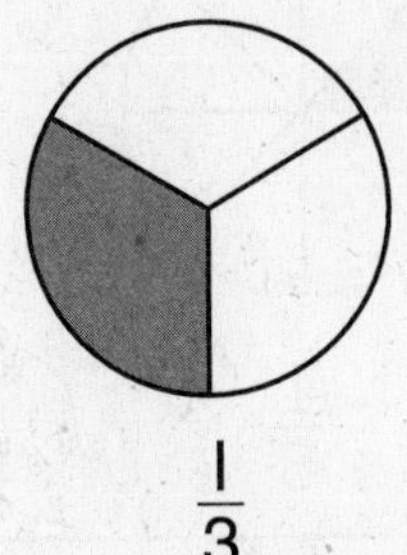

$\frac{1}{3}$

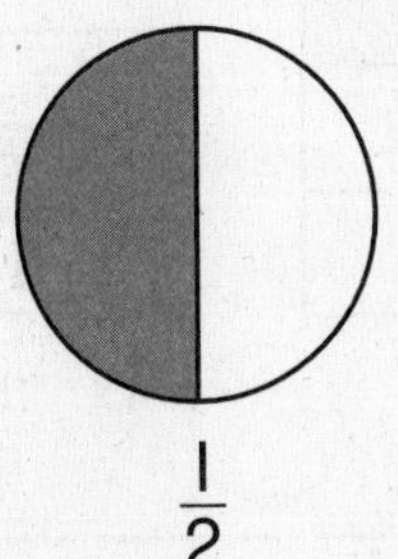

$\frac{1}{2}$

Compare the shaded parts. Then circle the fraction that is greater.

1.

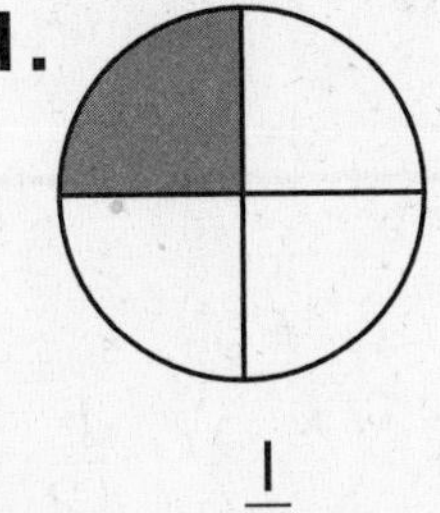

$\frac{1}{4}$

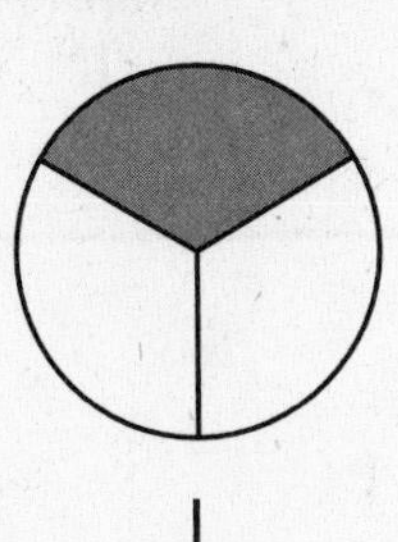

$\frac{1}{3}$

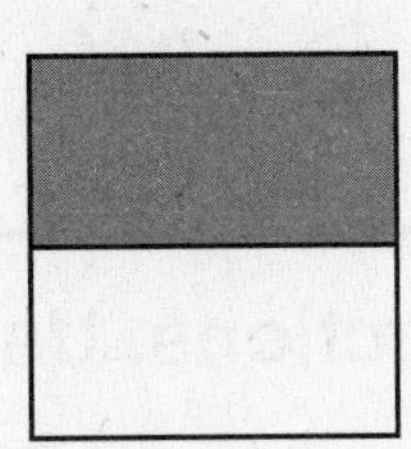

$\frac{1}{2}$

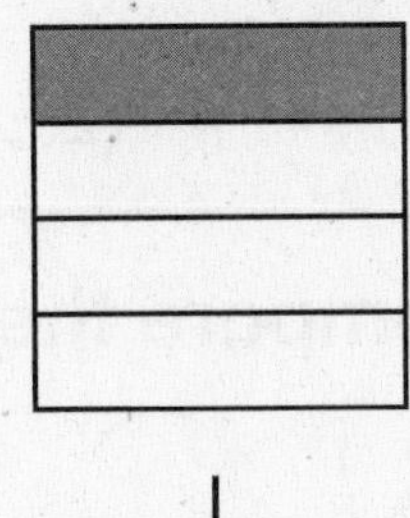

$\frac{1}{4}$

Compare the fractions. Then write < or >.

2.

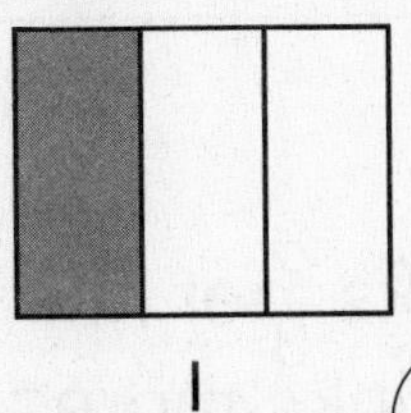

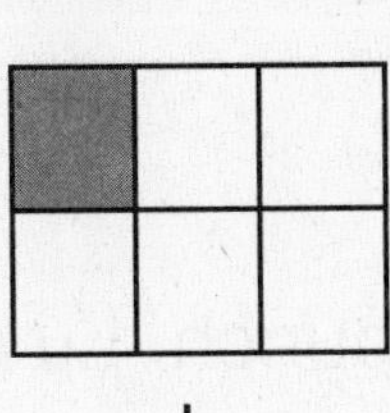

$\frac{1}{3}$ ◯ $\frac{1}{6}$

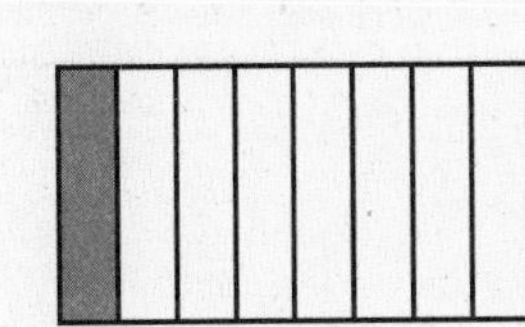

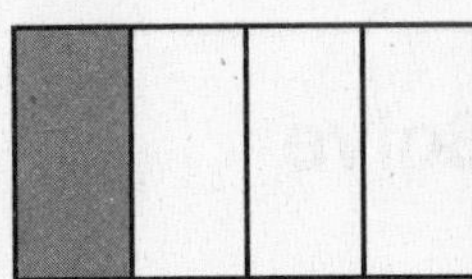

$\frac{1}{8}$ ◯ $\frac{1}{4}$

3.

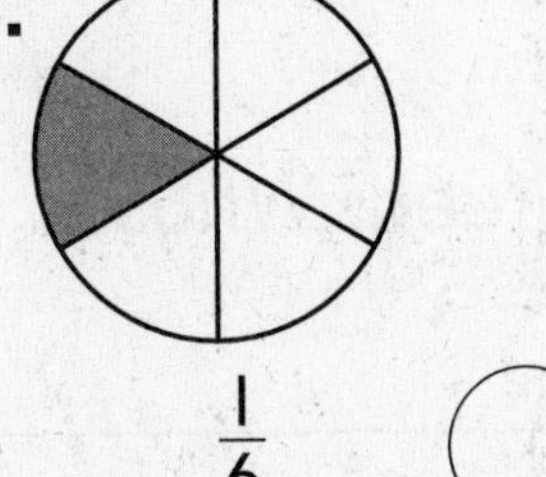

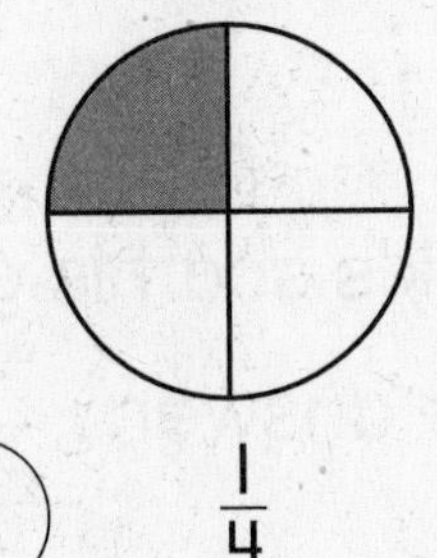

$\frac{1}{6}$ ◯ $\frac{1}{4}$

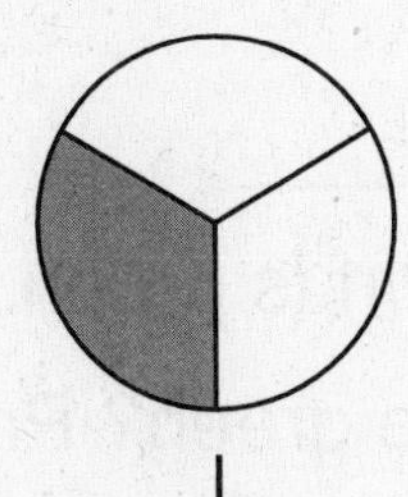

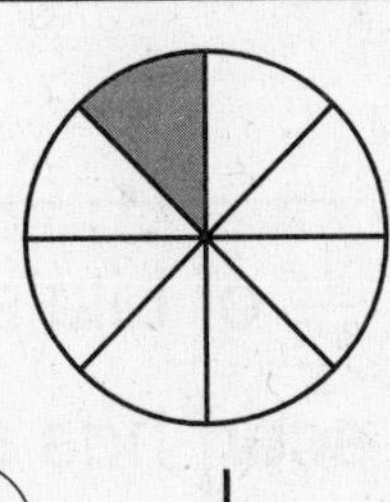

$\frac{1}{3}$ ◯ $\frac{1}{8}$

9-5

Name ____________________

Skills Practice

2NS4.2, 2MR1.2

Compare Fractions

Compare the fractions. Then write < or >.

1.

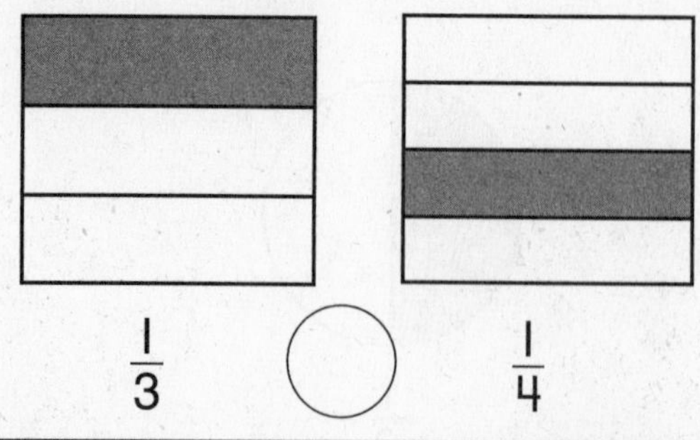

$\frac{1}{3}$ ◯ $\frac{1}{4}$

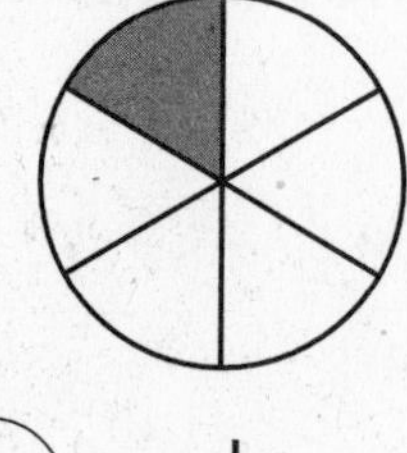

$\frac{1}{8}$ ◯ $\frac{1}{6}$

2.

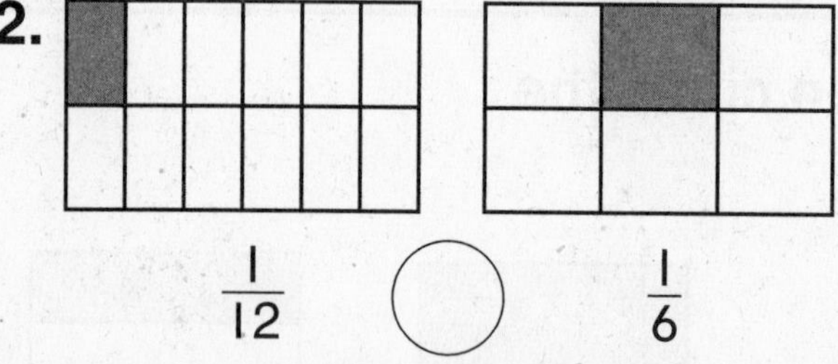

$\frac{1}{12}$ ◯ $\frac{1}{6}$

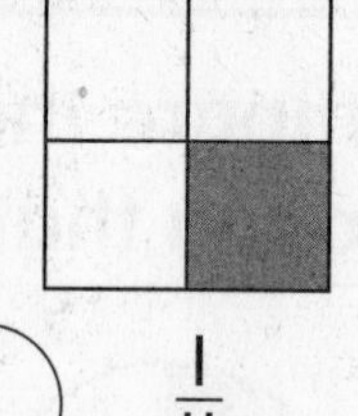

$\frac{1}{6}$ ◯ $\frac{1}{4}$

Compare the fractions. Use < or >.

3. $\frac{1}{3}$ 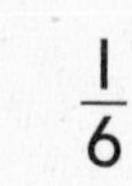 ◯ $\frac{1}{6}$

4. $\frac{1}{8}$  ◯ $\frac{1}{4}$

5. $\frac{1}{6}$ 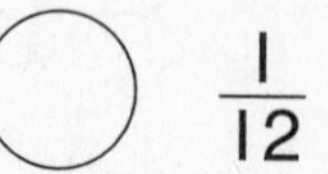 ◯ $\frac{1}{12}$

6. $\frac{1}{2}$ ◯ $\frac{1}{3}$

7. $\frac{1}{4}$ ◯ $\frac{1}{6}$

8. $\frac{1}{3}$ ◯ $\frac{1}{6}$

Solve

9. Lu and Marta each have a cup of punch. Lu drinks $\frac{2}{3}$ of her punch while Marta drinks $\frac{1}{2}$ of hers. Which girl drinks more punch? Explain.

____

10. $\frac{1}{12}$ of Lila's scarf is green. $\frac{1}{8}$ of Nick's scarf is green. Whose scarf has more green? Prove your answer.

____

Name ______________________________

9-6

Reteach

2NS4.2, 2MR1.2

Fractions of a Group

Chapter Resources

You can show a fraction of a group.

How many squares are white? _____

How many squares are there in all? _____

_____ of the squares are white.

_____ → white square

_____ → in all

Count squares to find the fraction.

1.

How many squares are white? _____

How many squares are there in all? _____

_____ of the squares are white.

_____ → white square

_____ → in all

2.

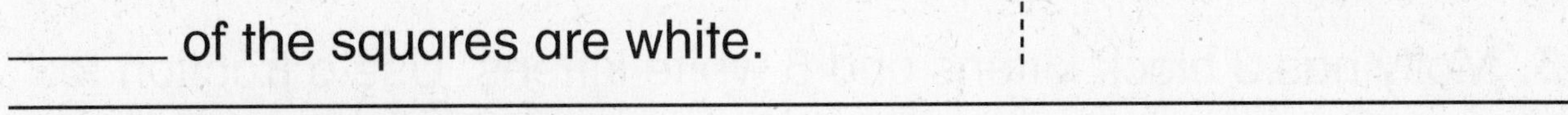

How many squares are white? _____

How many squares are there in all? _____

_____ of the squares are white.

_____ → white square

_____ → in all

3.

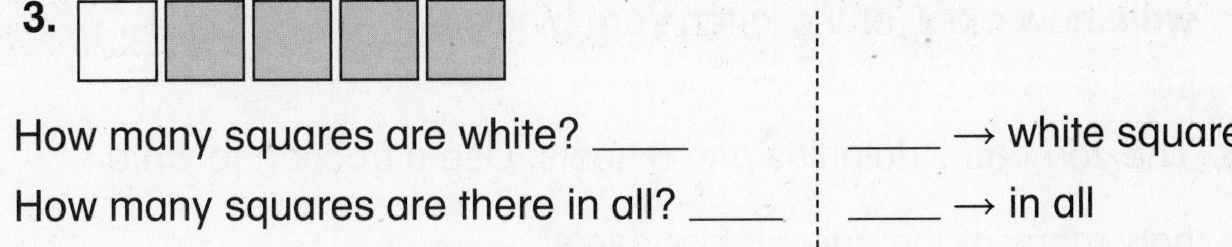

How many squares are white? _____

How many squares are there in all? _____

_____ of the squares are white.

_____ → white square

_____ → in all

9-6

Name ____________________

Skills Practice

2NS4.2, 2MR1.2

Unit Fractions of a Group

Write the fraction for the shaded part.

1. $\frac{5}{6}$ [handwritten]

2. ______

Look at the picture. Write the fraction.

3. What fraction of the animals are fish?

______ → total number of fish

______ → total number of animals

4. What fraction of the animals are dolphins?

______ → total number of dolphins

______ → total number of animals

Solve.

5. Molly has 3 black kittens and 5 white kittens. Use a fraction to write how many of the kittens are black. ______

6. The zoo has 7 dolphins and 5 seals. Use a fraction to write how many of the animals are seals. ______

Name ______________________________

Reteach

2NS4.2

Other Fractions of a Group

A fraction can name part of a group.

Circle the equal parts.

There are ______ equal parts.

What fraction of the fish are striped? ______ of 3 equal parts are striped.

The striped part is ______.

Circle the equal parts. Then write the fraction for the striped part.

1.  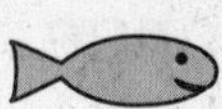 

______

2. 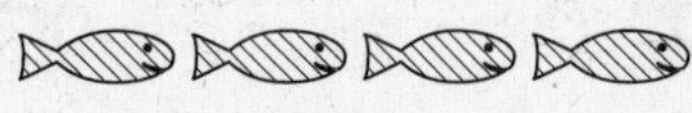

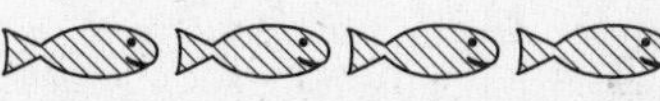

______

3.  

______

4. 

______

Name ________________________________

9-7

Skills Practice

2NS4.2

Other Fractions of a Group

Preparation: Crayons are needed for this activity.

Color to show the fraction of the group.

1. $\frac{5}{6}$ of the crayons are green.

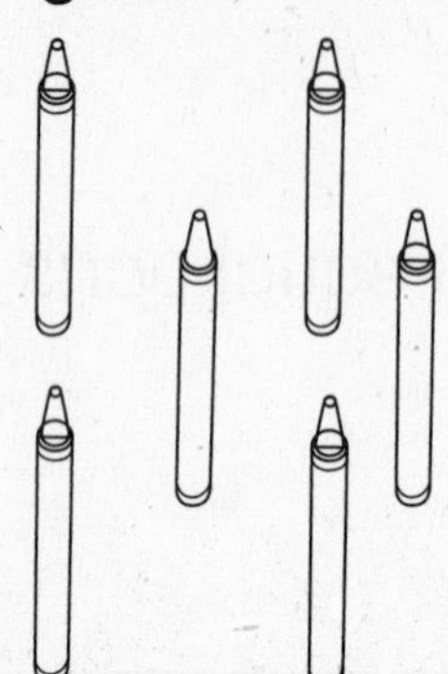

2. $\frac{3}{4}$ of the crayons are pink.

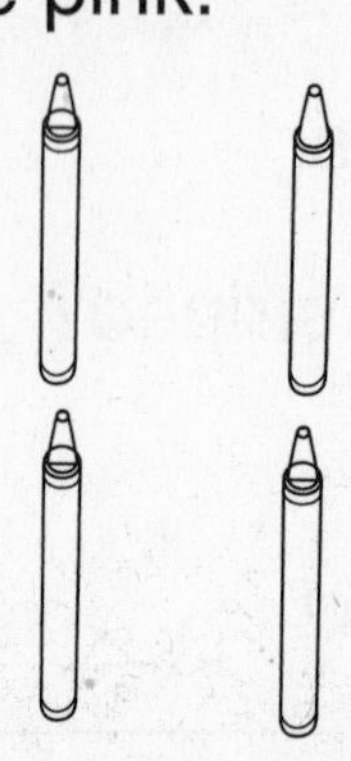

3. $\frac{3}{3}$ of the crayons are blue.

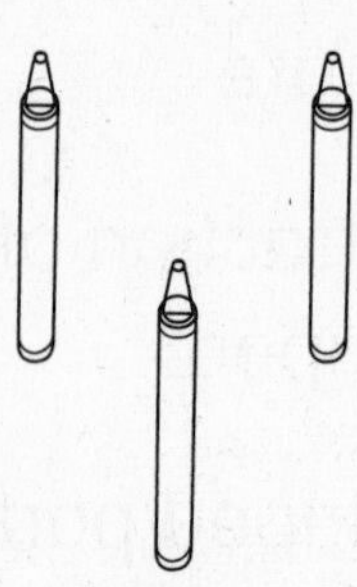

4. $\frac{3}{8}$ of the crayons are red.

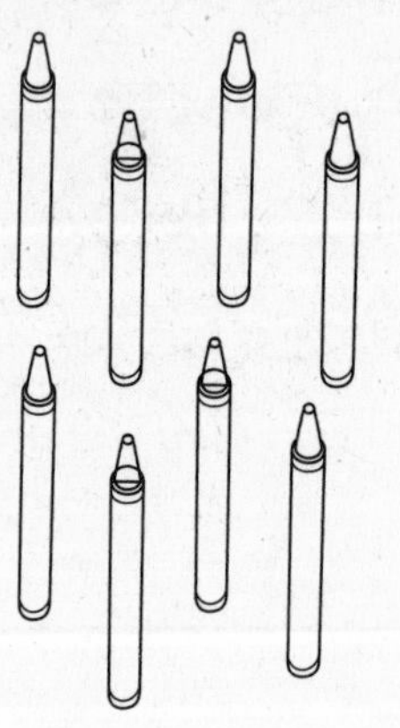

5. $\frac{1}{2}$ of the crayons are yellow.

6. $\frac{1}{6}$ of the crayons are orange.

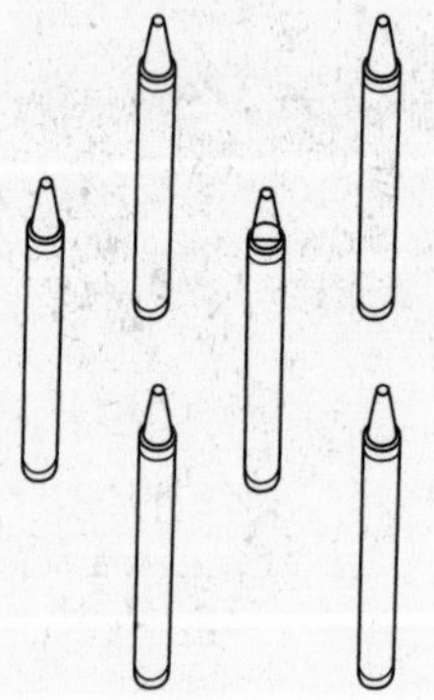

Solve.

7. Eric has three black dogs and one spotted dog. Write the fraction for the black dogs.

______

Name ____________________

9-8

Reteach (1)

2NS4.2, 2MR1.1

Problem-Solving Investigation: Choose a Strategy

Chapter Resources

Lin and her mom are buying eight pies.
Five of the pies are banana and the rest are apple.
What part of the pies are apple? Show your answer as a fraction.

Step 1
Understand

What do I know?

Lin and her mom are buying 8 pies.
Five pies are banana and the rest are apple.

What do I need to find out?

What part of the whole is apple.

Step 2
Plan

How will I find out?

I can write a number sentence.

If I subtract to find out how many pies are apple, I can find the part of the whole.

Step 3
Solve

Write a number sentence.

8 pies in all – 5 banana = 3 apple

3 parts of the whole are apple.

$\frac{3}{8}$ of the pies are apple.

Step 4
Check

Look back.

Did I check my answer to make sure it made sense?

Name ______________________________

9-8

Reteach (2)

2NS4.2, 2MR1.1

Problem-Solving Investigation: Choose a Strategy

Choose a strategy to answer each question.

Problem-Solving Strategies
- Use a Pattern
- Write a Number Sentence
- Make a Table

1. Johnson's pet shop has 4 cages. Each cage can hold 3 kittens. How many kittens are in Johnson's pet shop?

   ______ kittens

2. There were 16 birds in the park. 12 of the birds were crows and the others were ducks. What fraction of the birds were ducks?

   ______

   Which is greater, the fraction of birds that are crows or ducks?

   Explain. ______________________________

3. There are 8 children on the beach. 3 are swimming and 5 are playing tag. What fraction of children are swimming? ______

   What fraction of children are playing tag? ______

4. Marie plants 12 flowers. Four flowers are tulips. The other flowers are daisies. What fraction shows how many flowers are daisies?

   ______

Name ______________________________

9-8

Skills Practice

2NS4.2, 2MR1.1

Problem-Solving Investigation: Choose a Strategy

Chapter Resources

Choose a strategy to answer each question.

Problem-Solving Strategies
- Use a Pattern
- Write a Number Sentence
- Make a Table

1. David has 12 fish. 4 of his fish are yellow and 4 are orange. How many spotted fish does David have?

_____ spotted fish

2. Alma cut a melon in halves. She shared one-half with her brother. Her grandparents shared the rest. How much of the melon did Alma eat? _____

3. Megan breaks a muffin into 3 equal pieces. She eats 2 pieces. What fraction of the muffin did she eat?

_____

4. Juan buys 15 marbles to give to friends. He gives 5 marbles to Abby. He gives 6 marbles to Lou. He gives the rest to Jon. What fraction shows how many marbles Jon has?

_____

5. Eve has 13 strawberries. She puts 9 in a tart. She eats the rest. How many strawberries does Eve eat?

_____ strawberries

Name ____________________

Reteach

2NS1.0, 2MR1.2

Hundreds

Preparation: Scissors and glue are needed for this activity.

Cut the tens and hundreds below. Glue to show the number.

1. 4 tens = 40 ones

2. 6 tens = 60 ones

3. 2 hundreds = 20 tens = 200 ones

4. 3 hundreds = 30 tens = 300 ones

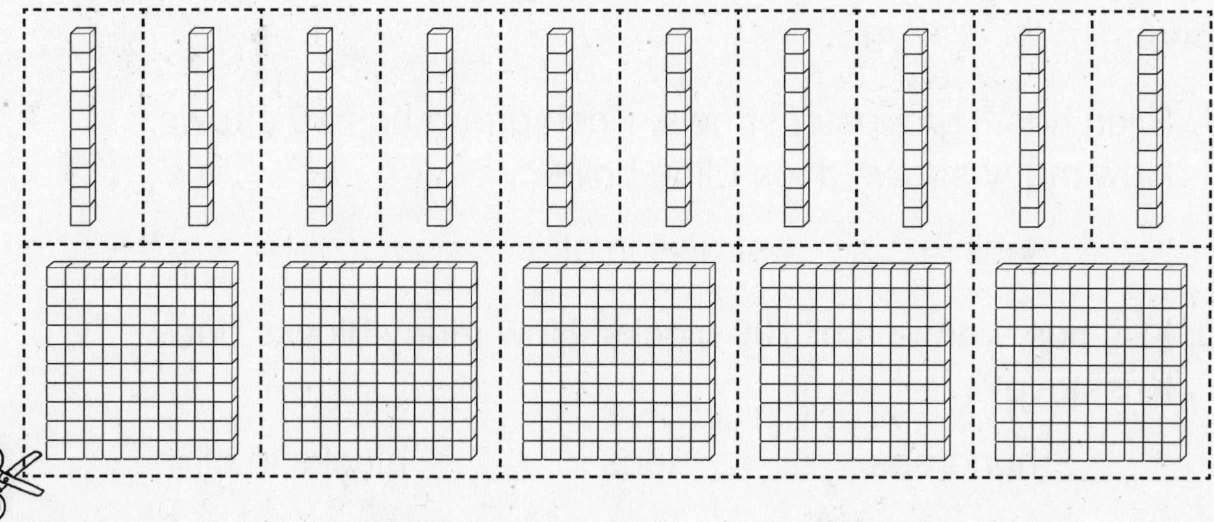

Name ______________________

10-1

Skills Practice

2NS1.0

Hundreds

Write how many.

1. 6 groups of ten

6 tens = 60 ones

2. 9 groups of ten

9 tens = ______ ones

3. 4 groups of one hundred

______ hundreds =

______ tens = ______ ones

4. 2 groups of one hundred

______ hundreds =

______ tens = ______ ones

5. 7 groups of one hundred

______ hundreds =

______ tens = ______ ones

6. 1 group of one hundred

______ hundred =

______ tens = ______ ones

7. 5 groups of one hundred

______ hundreds =

______ tens = ______ ones

8. 8 groups of one hundred

______ hundreds =

______ tens = ______ ones

Solve.

9. Elian has 3 groups of straws. Each group has 10 straws. How many straws does Elian have?

______ tens = ______ straws in all

10. Kris has 4 groups of 100 blocks. How many blocks does Kris have?

______ hundreds = ______ tens = ______ blocks in all

Name ______________________

10-2

Reteach

2NS1.1, 2NS1.2

Hundreds, Tens, and Ones

Chapter Resources

You can use pictures to represent hundreds, tens, and ones.

126	1 hundred	2 tens	6 ones

Write and draw how many hundreds, tens, and ones.

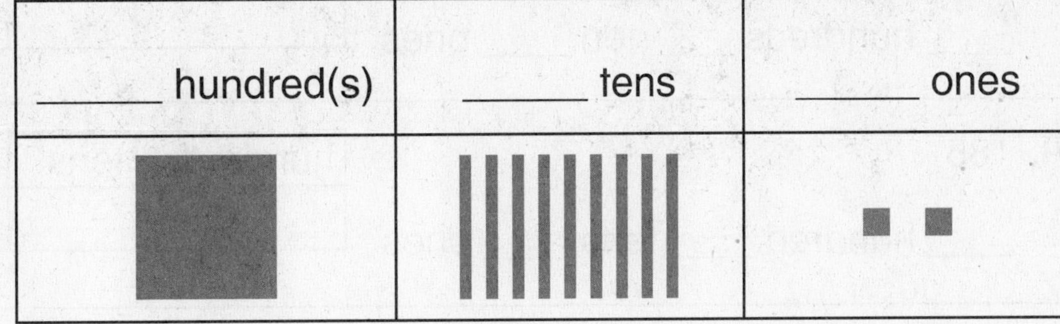

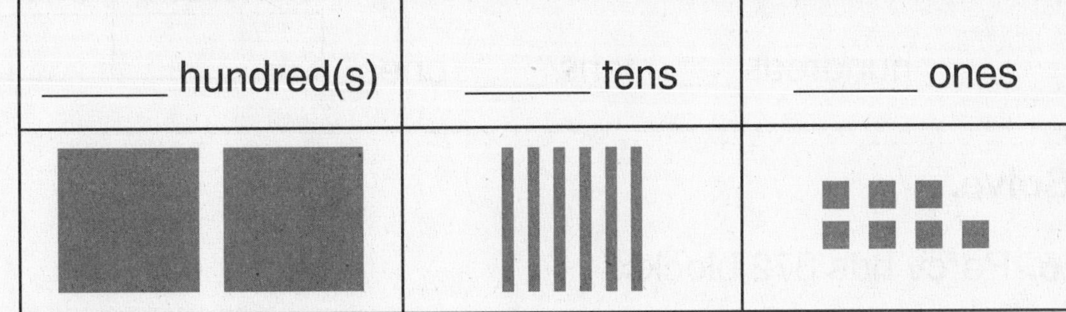

Write the number.

3. 3 hundreds 2 tens 5 ones = _______

4. 2 hundreds 4 tens 9 ones = _______

5. 8 hundreds 7 tens 0 ones = _______

Name ______________________________

10-2

Skills Practice

2NS1.1, 2NS1.2

Hundreds, Tens, and Ones

Write how many hundreds, tens, and ones.

1. 736

7 hundreds 3 tens 6 ones

hundreds	tens	ones
7	3	6

2. 263

____ hundreds ____ tens ____ ones

hundreds	tens	ones

3. 518

____ hundreds ____ ten ____ ones

hundreds	tens	ones

4. 185

____ hundred ____ tens ____ ones

hundreds	tens	ones

5. 360

____ hundreds ____ tens ____ ones

hundreds	tens	ones

Solve.

6. Percy has 372 blocks.
How many tens does he have? ______ tens

7. Luis has 613 beads.
How many hundreds does he have? ______ hundreds

8. Dana has 490 stickers.
How many tens does she have? ______ tens

Name ______________________________

10-3

Reteach (1)

2MR2.2, 2SDAP1.1

Problem-Solving Strategy: Make a List

Each roller coaster car seats 3 children.
Will, Mateo, and Li want to sit in the same car.
How many different ways can they sit?

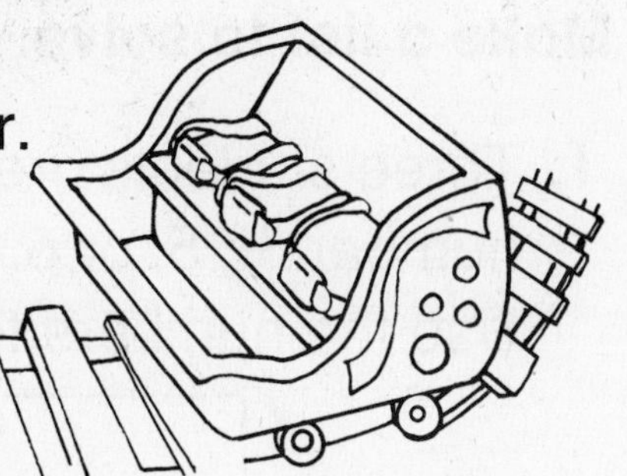

Step 1
Understand

What do I know?

There are 3 children.
Their names are Will, Mateo, and Li.
They want to sit in the same car.

What do I need to find out?

How many different ways can they sit?

Step 2
Plan

How will I find out?

I will make a list of all ways to sit.
A list is a clear way to show names or numbers.

Step 3
Solve

Make a list.

Will, Mateo, Li	Mateo, Will, Li	Li, Will, Mateo
Will, Li, Mateo	Mateo, Li, Will	Li, Mateo, Will

There are __6__ ways to sit.

Step 4
Check

Look Back

How can I be sure that I found all ways to sit?

Name ______________________

10-3

Reteach (2)

2MR2.2, 2SDAP1.1

Problem-Solving Strategy: Make a List

Make a list to solve. Show your work.

1. Three students are running a race. Each student is wearing a number: 4, 5, or 6. The students can finish first, middle, or last. Use the numbers to find out how many ways the race can end.

There are ______ ways for the race to end.

2. Olive is coloring 3 flowers in a row. She is using her blue, yellow, and red crayons. How many ways can she color the flowers?

There are ______ ways to color the flowers.

3. Abdul has tomato seeds and pepper seeds. He can put each in a clay pot or a plastic pot. How many different plant pots can he make?

Abdul can make ______ different plant pots.

Name ______________________________

10-3

Skills Practice

2MR2.2, 2SDAP1.1

Problem-Solving Strategy: Make a List

Chapter Resources

Preparation: A separate piece of paper is needed for this activity.

Make a list to solve. Use a separate piece of paper.

1. Chen chooses where people sit at the picnic. He has 3 seats in a row for Mom, Lien, and Roy. How many different ways can they sit? Write them.

   ____

   ____

   ____

   They can sit in ______ different ways.

2. Nina is making a birdhouse. Birdhouse kits come in 3 sizes: big, medium, and small. She can choose from white, blue, or pink paint. How many different birdhouses can Nina make?

   Nina can make ______ different birdhouses.

3. A kite tail has space for 3 bows. Rob has a green bow, a blue bow, and a gold bow. How many different ways can Rob tie the bows?

   Rob can tie the bows in ______ different ways.

4. Lupé lost her classroom number. She remembers that it has the numbers 2, 3, and 4. How many different three-digit numbers could she try?

   Write them. ______, ______, ______, ______, ______, ______

   Lupé could try ______ rooms.

10-4

Name ______________________________

Reteach

2NS1.1, 2NS1.2

Place Value to 1,000

Chapter Resources

Expanded form shows how many thousands, hundreds, tens, and ones.
Match each number to the correct expanded form.

1. 345	900 + 10 + 5
2. 721	200 + 70 + 8
3. 166	700 + 20 + 1
4. 915	800 + 30 + 7
5. 584	300 + 40 + + 5
6. 439	600 + 90 + 0
7. 278	100 + 60 + 6
8. 690	1000 + 0 + 0 + 0
9. 837	500 + 80 + 4
10. 1,000	400 + 30 + 9

Name ____________________

10-4

Skills Practice

2NS1.1, 2NS1.2

Place Value to 1,000

Write how many thousands, hundreds, tens, and ones. Then write the number.

1.

Thousands	Hundreds	Tens	Ones

______ thousand ______ hundreds ______ tens ______ ones

________ + ______ + ______ + ______ = __________

2.

Thousands	Hundreds	Tens	Ones

______ thousand ______ hundreds ______ tens ______ ones

__________ + __________ + __________ = __________

Solve.

3. The theater sells 142 tickets. Show how many tickets were sold in expanded form.

______ + ______ + ______ = 142 tickets

4. An airplane flies 640 miles. How many hundreds?

__________ hundreds

Name ________________________________

10-5

Reteach

2NS1.1, 2NS1.2

Read and Write Numbers to 1,000

Chapter Resources

Preparation: Scissors and glue are needed for this activity.

Words can tell numbers.
Cut and glue words to match the numbers.

1. 496

2. 937

3. 1,000

4. 188

5. 350

6. 625

one hundred eighty-eight	one thousand
four hundred ninety-six	three hundred fifty
nine hundred thirty-seven	six hundred twenty-five

Name ______________________________

10-5

Skills Practice

2NS1.1, 2NS1.2

Read and Write Numbers to 1,000

Read the number. Write it in 2 different ways.

1. 300 + 70 + 2

____

hundreds	tens	ones

2. eight hundred forty-one

_______ + _______ + _______ = _______

hundreds	tens	ones

Circle the correct number word.

3. 975

nine hundred fifty-seven

nine hundred seventy-five

4. 193

one hundred ninety-three

one hundred ninety

Solve.

5. There are 429 students at Linden School. Cora wants to write the number in words for a newsletter. What should she write?

______________________________ students

6. Marco lives at nine hundred thirty-one Maple Street. Use expanded form to show Marco's address.

_______ + _______ + _______ = _______ Maple Street

Name ______________________________

10-6

Reteach (1)

2NS2.0, 2MR1.1

Problem-Solving Investigation: Choose a Strategy

Chapter Resources

Preparation: Base-ten blocks are needed for this activity.

The bakers at Barry's Bakery baked 238 bagels.
Then, they baked 20 more bagels.
Write the number name for the number of bagels baked in all.

Step 1 Understand

What do I know?

The bakers baked 238 bagels.

They baked 20 more.

What do I need to find out?

The number of bagels baked in all.

Step 2 Plan

How will I find out?

You can use a model to find the difference.

Step 3 Solve

Use a model.

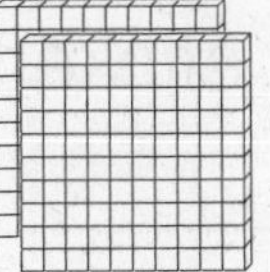

Hundreds **Tens** **Ones**

The bakers baked

______________________________ bagels.

Step 4 Check

Look Back.

Did I use a model to count the bagels?
Does my model show how many were added?

Name ______________________________

10-6

Reteach (2)

2NS2.0, 2MR1.1

Problem-Solving Investigation: Choose a Strategy

Preparation: Access to base-ten blocks is needed for this activity.

Solve.

Problem-Solving Strategies
Make an organized list
Write a number sentence
Use a model

1. Carmen has 659 blocks. How many hundreds, tens, and ones are her blocks in groups of?

____

____

2. Pat's Fruit Stand has 534 peaches for sale. Pat sells 30 peaches this afternoon.

How many peaches are left to sell?

______ peaches

3. Lucy is thinking of a number. Her number is greater than two hundred twenty-five. Her number is less than 2 hundreds 2 tens 7 ones. What is Lucy's number?

______

What number is ten more than Lucy's number?

______

What number is one hundred less than lucy's number?

______

4. Ralph has 957 star stickers. He gave 10 to Ken. Write the words that tell how many star stickers Ralph has left.

____

____

What if Ralph gave Ken 100 stickers instead? Write that number in words.

____

____

Name ______________________________

10-6

Skills Practice

2NS2.0, 2MR1.1

Problem-Solving Investigation: Choose a Strategy

Preparation: Access to base-ten blocks is needed for this activity.

Solve.

Problem-Solving Strategies
Make an organized list
Write a number sentence
Use a model

1. Naomi is playing a word game. She must write down how many ways to combine the letters N, O, and T. How many ways are there?

There are ______ ways for Naomi to combine N, O, and T.

2. Maria's bean jar has less than 734 beans. The jar has greater than 732 beans. What is the number word for how many beans in Maria's jar?

____

______________ beans

3. Franklin writes the number word four hundred ninety-one. If he shows the number in cubes, how many tens will there be? ______

4. Jin's family brings three hundred twenty-five tarts to the bake sale. They sell ten this morning. How many tarts are left to sell? ______

Name ______________________

10-7

Reteach

2NS1.3

Compare Numbers

Chapter Resources

Pictures can show how some numbers are greater than others.

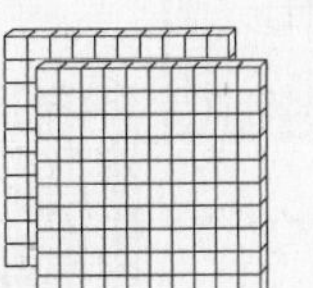 217

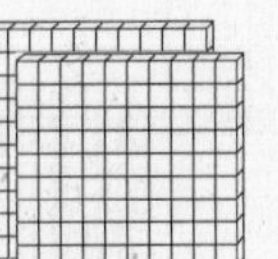 (221)

Look at each picture. Write the number that shows how many cubes. Then, circle the number that is greater.

1. 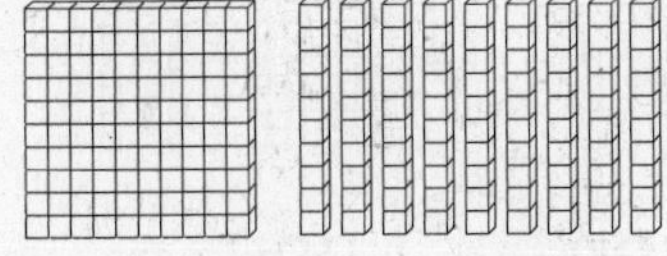 ______ 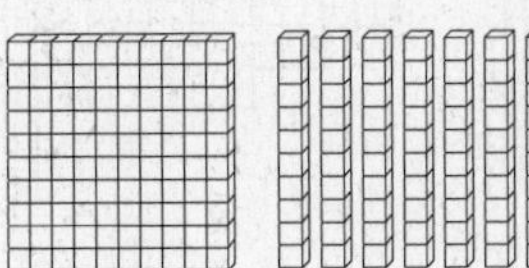 ______

2. 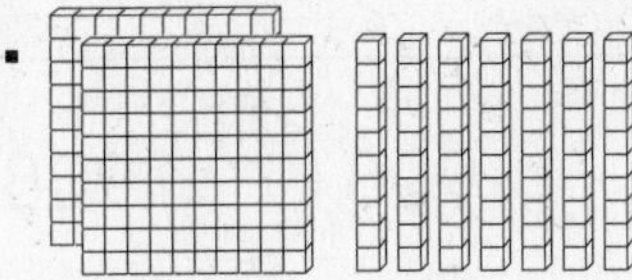 ______ 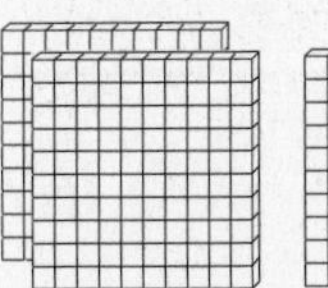 ______

3. 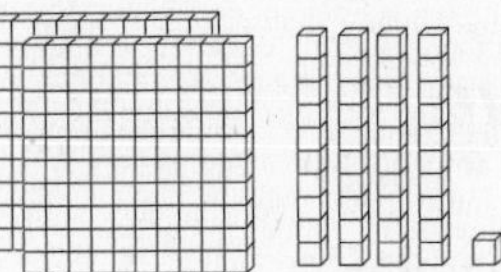 ______ ______

4. 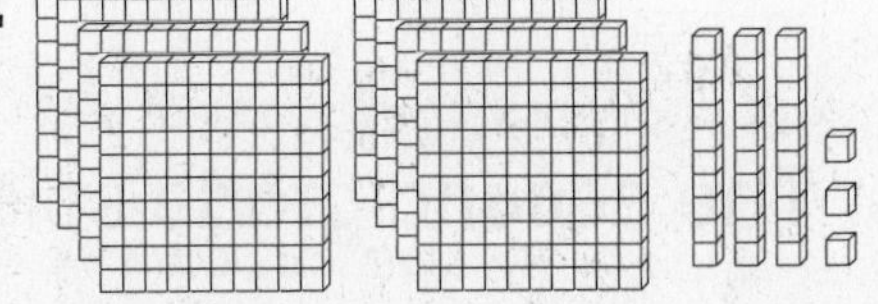 ______ 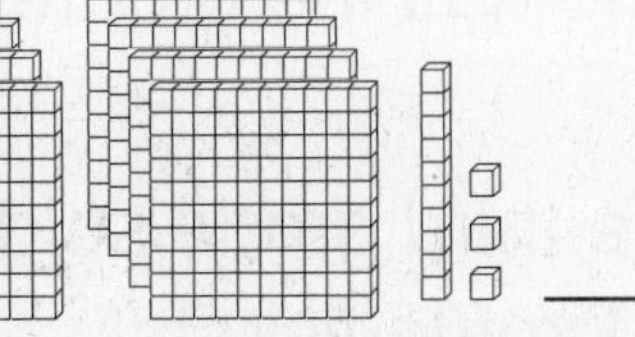 ______

5. 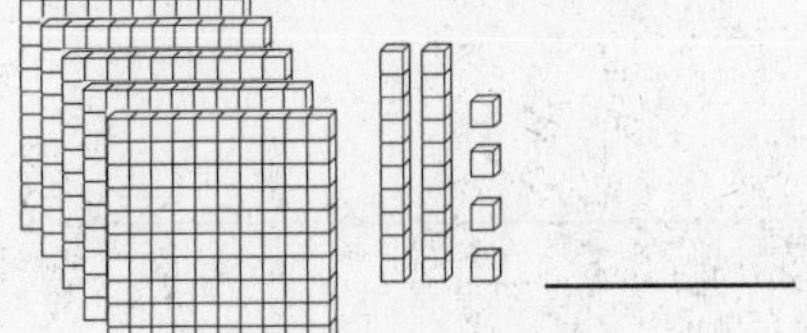 ______ ______

Name ______________________

10-7

Skills Practice

Compare Numbers

2NS1.3

Compare. Write >, <, =.

1.

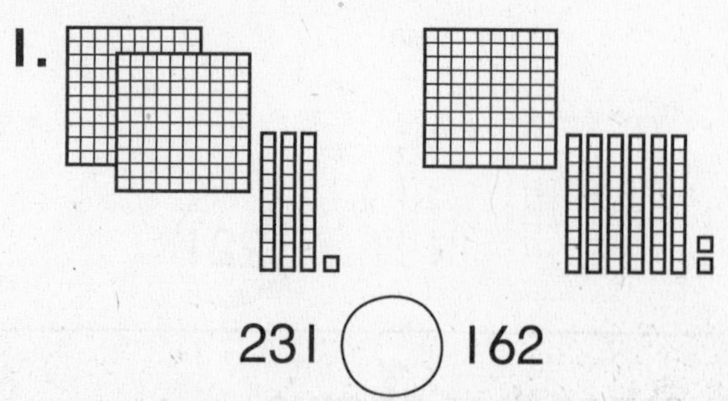

231 ◯ 162

2.

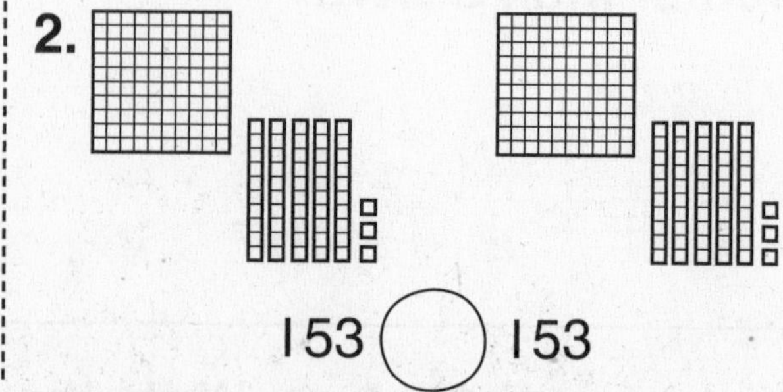

153 ◯ 153

3.

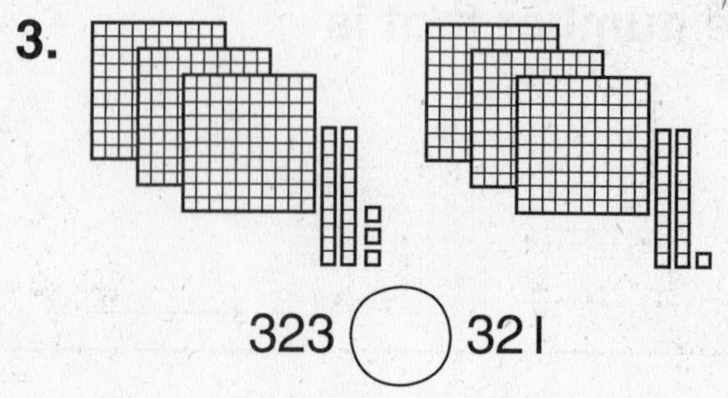

323 ◯ 321

4.

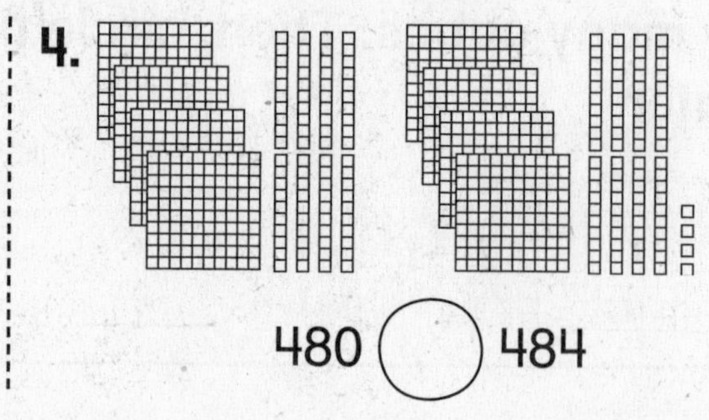

480 ◯ 484

5. 278 ◯ 287 | 679 ◯ 677 | 908 ◯ 908

Write *greater than, less than,* or *equal to.* Solve.

6. Ms. Smith has 541 books. Mr. Costa has 529 books.

541 is ____________________ 529.

Who has the greater number of books? ________________

7. The third grade sold 239 raffle tickets. The second grade sold 401 raffle tickets.

239 is ________________ 401.

Which grade sold less raffle tickets? ____________________

Name ____________________

10-8

Reteach

2NS1.3

Order Numbers

Chapter Resources

Place value can help order numbers from *greatest* to *least*.

823, **8**32, **9**32	First, compare hundreds.
932, ___, ___	**9**32 is greater than **8**23 and **8**32.
932, 8**3**2, 8**2**3.	Then, compare tens. 8**3**2 is greater than 8**2**3.

Write the numbers from *greatest* to *least*. Use place value to order the numbers.

1. 602, 612, 206

_______, _______, _______

2. 879, 897, 987

_______, _______, _______

3. 301, 130, 103

_______, _______, _______

4. 455, 545, 544

_______, _______, _______

5. 728, 287, 872

_______, _______, _______

6. 139, 109, 301, 391

_______, _______, _______, _______

7. 217, 720, 721, 127

_______, _______, _______, _______

Name ___________________________________

10-8

Skills Practice

2NS1.3

Order Numbers

Order the numbers from *greatest* to *least*.

1. 354, 674, 359 ___674___, __________, __________

2. 592, 952, 951 __________, __________, __________

3. 808, 873, 782 __________, __________, __________

Order the numbers from *least* to *greatest*.

4. 423, 444, 324 __________, __________, __________

5. 192, 157, 132 __________, __________, __________

6. 745, 867, 748 __________, __________, __________

7. 168, 186, 166 __________, __________, __________

Solve.

8. Sen's 4 friends live on the same street. She write down their house numbers.

234 1423 324 403

How can Sen write the house numbers from *greatest* to *least*?

__________, __________, __________, __________

9. Now Sen wants to write the house numbers from *least* to *greatest*. What should the second house number be? ________

Name ______

10-9

Reteach

2SDAP2.0

Number Patterns

Chapter Resources

You can use number patterns to help you count.

Count by tens.

340, 350, ______, 370, ______, 390

Count by hundreds.

400, 500, 600, ______, 800, ______

Write the missing numbers.
Then circle the counting pattern.

	Pattern—Count by:	
1. 220, 230, ______, 250, ______, 270, 280	tens	hundreds
2. 510, 520, 530, ______, 550, ______, 570	tens	hundreds
3. 135, 145, 155, ______, 175, ______, 195	tens	hundreds
4. 747, 757, ______, ______, 787, 797, 807	tens	hundreds
5. 200, 300, 400, ______, 600, ______, 800	tens	hundreds
6. 350, 450, 550, ______, ______, 850, 950	tens	hundreds
7. 182, ______, 382, 482, ______, 682, 782	tens	hundreds

Name ______________________________

10-9

Skills Practice

2SDAP2.0

Number Patterns

Write the missing numbers. Then write the pattern.

1. 715, 725, 735, 745, 755

   Each number is __________.

2. 491, ______, 691, ______, 891

   Each number is __________.

3. ______, 839, ______, 837, 836

   Each number is __________.

4. ______, 595, 495, 395, ______

   Each number is __________.

5. 599, 589, 579, ______, ______

   Each number is __________.

Use the pattern to solve.

6. The numbers have fallen off of two houses on Ivy Street. Write the missing house numbers.

   345, 355, ______, 375, ______, 395.

7. Five students are lined up for a race. Each student is wearing a number. Which students are missing?

   708, 608, 508, ______, 308, ______

11-1

Name ______________________

Reteach

2MG2.0

Solid Shapes

Preparation: Crayons are needed for this activity.

Color each shape the correct color.

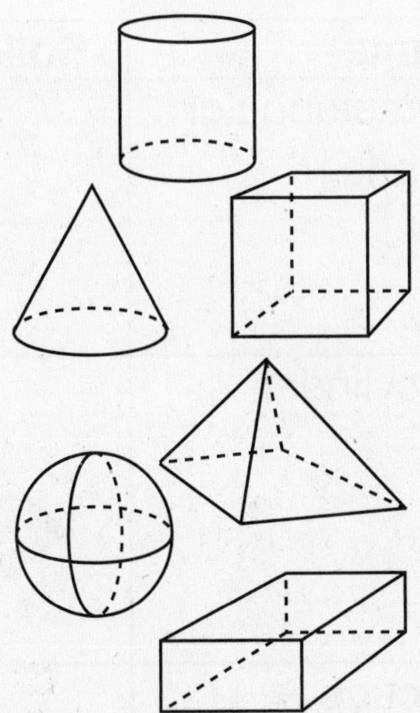

1. Color the **cone** red.
2. Color the **pyramid** blue.
3. Color the **sphere** green.
4. Color the **cube** yellow.
5. Color the **cylinder** purple.
6. Color the **rectangular prism** orange.

---

7. Draw a yellow line around the cone. Then draw a red line around the sphere.

8. Find the cubes in the picture. Draw a line around them.

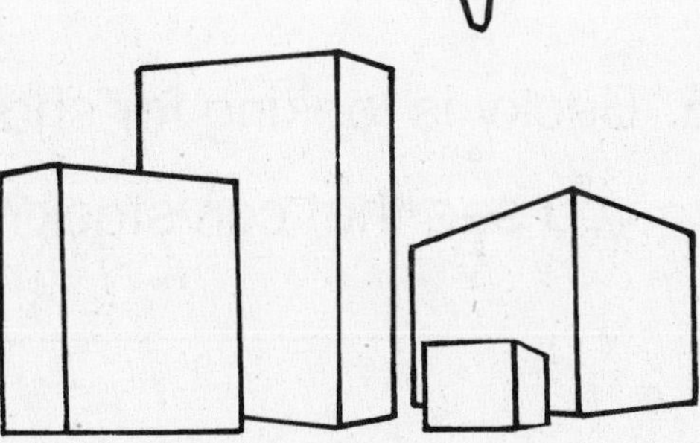

Name

11-1

Skills Practice

2MG2.0

Solid Shapes

Circle the solid shape. Write the name of something in your classroom or outside that is this shape.

Name	Solid Figure
1. rectangular prism	
2. cylinder	
3. cube	

Solve.

4. Look over this page. Ryan's soup can looks like one of these shapes. What shape is Ryan's soup can? ______________

5. Becky is looking for shapes that can stack. What shapes do you see that can stack? ______________

____

11-2

Name ______________________________

Reteach

2MG2.1, 2MR1.2

Faces, Edges, and Vertices

Preparation: Crayons are needed for this activity.

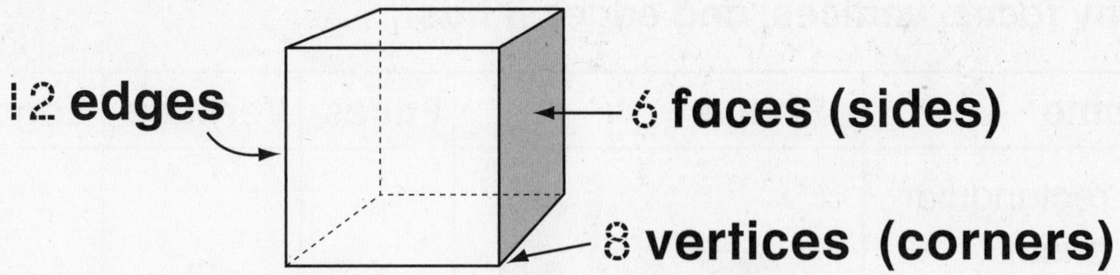

Write how many faces, vertices, and edges.

	Solid Figure	Faces	Vertices	Edges
1.				
2.				

3. Find the figure that has one face and a point. Color it blue.

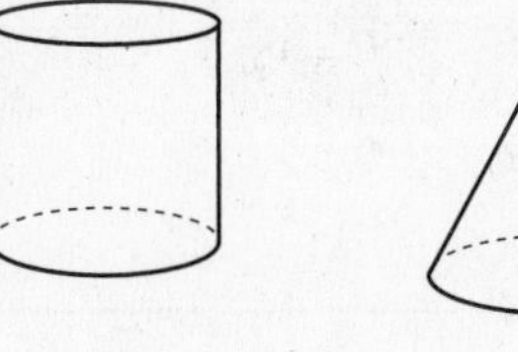

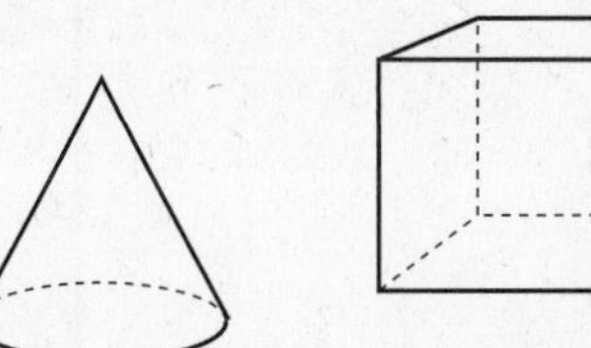

4. Find the figures with the same number of faces. Color them red.

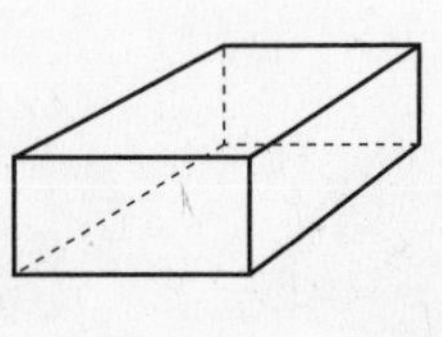

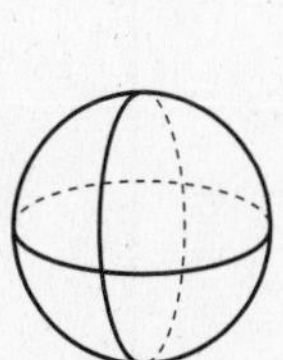

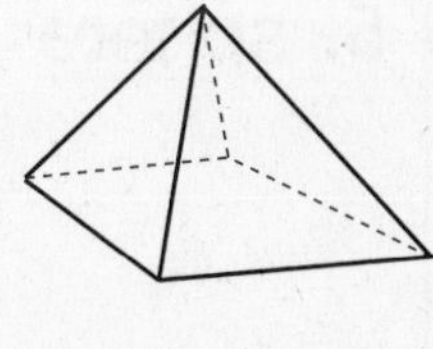

5. Circle the figures that can roll.

Name ________________________________

11-2

Skills Practice

2MG2.1, 2MR1.2

Faces, Edges, and Vertices

Circle the solid shape that is named. Write how many faces, vertices, and edges it has.

Name	Shape	Faces	Vertices	Edges
1. rectangular prism		6	8	
2. cone				
3. cube				
4. pyramid				
5. sphere				

Name ______________________________

11-3

Reteach

2MG2.0

Plane Shapes

A plane shape is a 2-dimensional figure with only length and width.

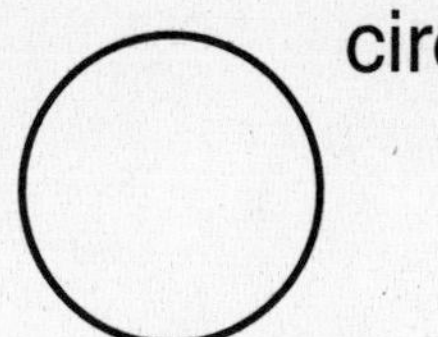
circle

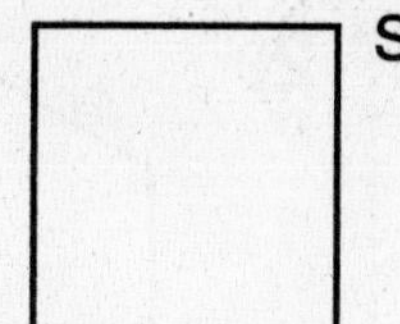
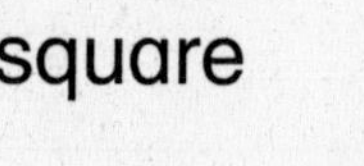
square

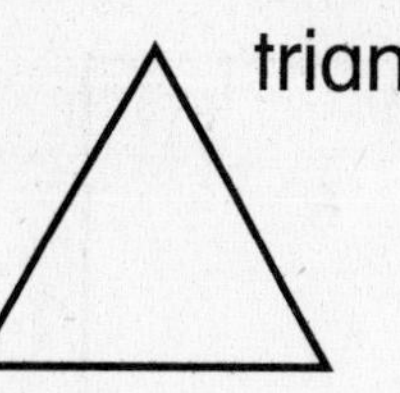
triangle

parallelogram

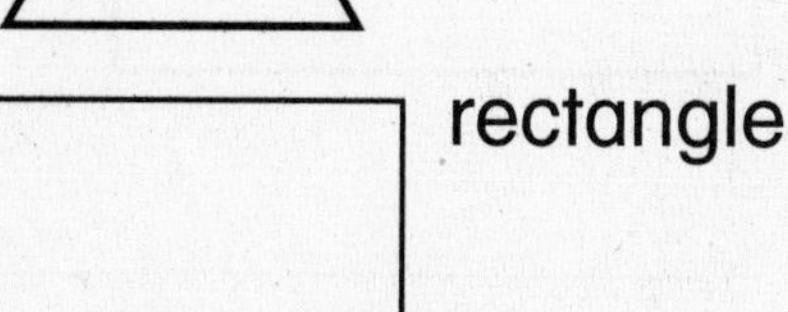
rectangle

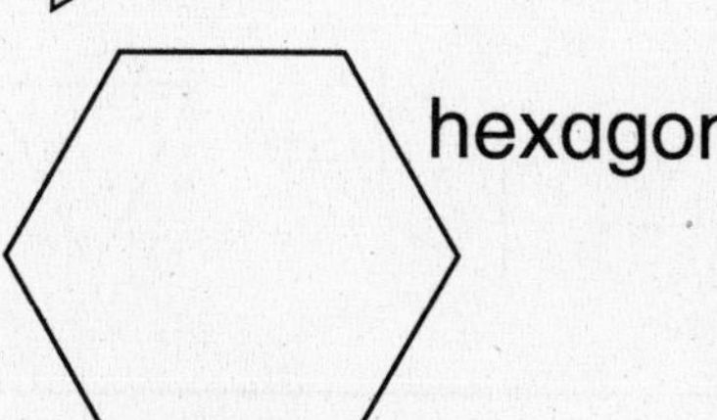
hexagon

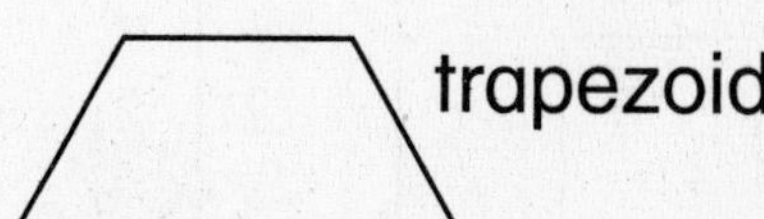
trapezoid

---

1. Draw a line from the shape to its name.

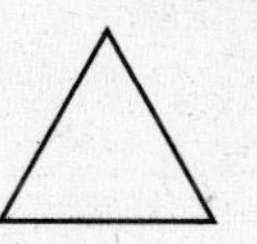
trapezoid

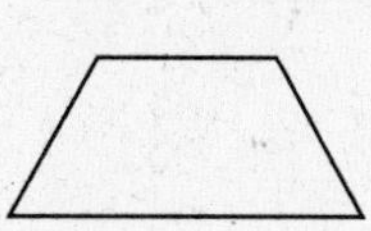
rectangle

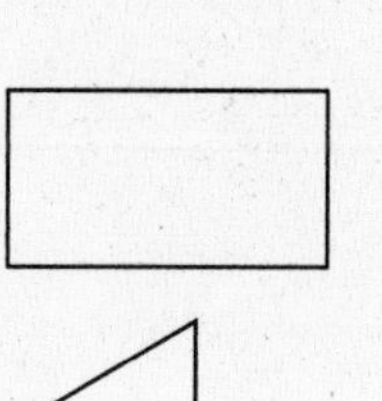
triangle

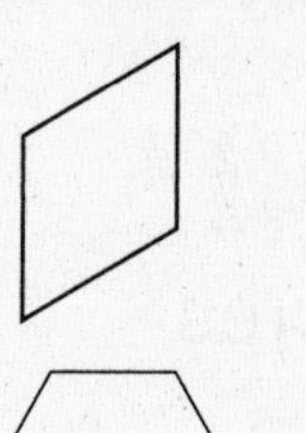
hexagon

parallelogram

11-3

Name ______________________

Skills Practice

2MG2.0

Plane Shapes

Write the name of the figure. Then circle the object that matches the figure.

1.

____

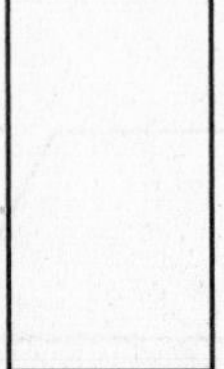
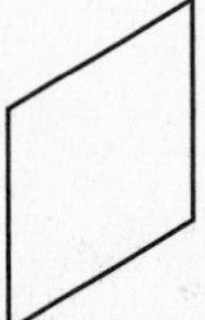

2.

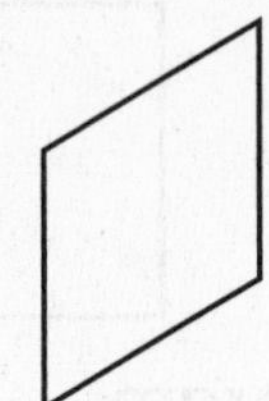

____

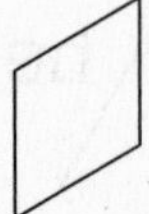

3.

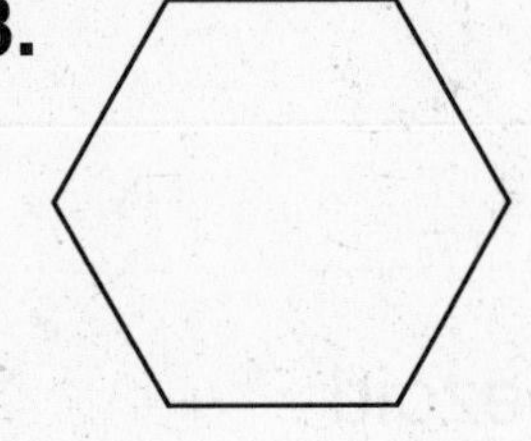

____

4.

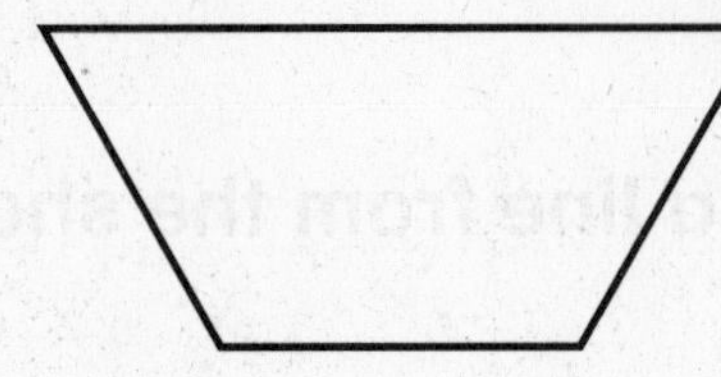

____

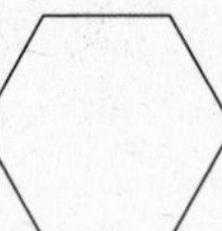

Pat drew this picture.

5.

How many circles? _____ circles

How many squares? _____ squares

How many rectangles? _____ rectangles

Name ______________________________

Reteach (1)

2MR1.0, 2SDAP2.1

Problem-Solving Strategy: Find a Pattern

Chapter Resources

Dee is making a pattern out of blocks.
She places a cone, a cube, a pyramid, a cone, and a cube.
What block comes next?

Step 1
Understand

What do I know?

Dee made a pattern.
She used a cone, a cube, a pyramid, a cone, and a cube.

What do I need to find out?

What block comes next.

Step 2
Plan

How will I find the block that comes next?

I will find a pattern.

Step 3
Solve

Find a pattern.

 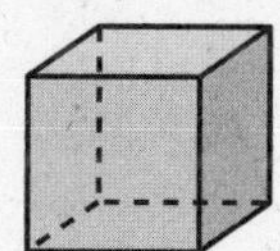 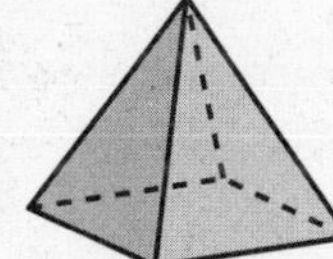  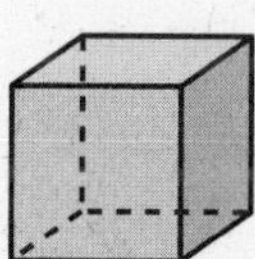

What shape comes next? pyramid

Step 4
Check

Look back.

Does my answer make sense? yes
Can I check my answer?

____

Name ____________________

11-4

Reteach (2)

2MR1.0, 2SDAP2.1

Problem-Solving Strategy: Find a Pattern

Find a pattern to solve. Write your answer.

1. Dave is making a pattern with blocks. He has [cylinder] [pyramid] [cylinder] [pyramid]. What shape comes next?

____

2. Jan is making a pattern with blocks. She has a cube, a sphere, a cube, and a sphere. What shape comes next?

____

3. Randy is making a pattern with blocks. He has a sphere, a cylinder, a rectangular prism, a sphere, and a cylinder. What will be the 7th shape?

____

4. Rosa says she sees a pattern in the shapes of the signs on her street. She sees a rectangle, a square, a square, a rectangle, a square, and a square. Is she right?

____

Name ______________________________

Skills Practice

2MR1.0, 2SDAP2.1

Problem-Solving Strategy: Find a Pattern

Find a pattern to solve. Write your answer.

1. Josh is drawing shapes.

   He draws  .

   Is he drawing a pattern? ______________

2. Leo sees this pattern on a poster.

   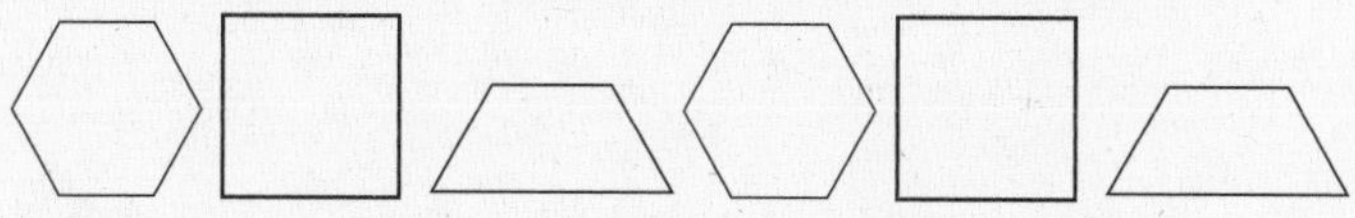

   What three shapes come next?

   ________ ________ ________

3. Martha is coloring a row of circles. She colors them red, blue, blue, red, blue, and blue. Is there a pattern? ______ Write the pattern. ________________________

4. One elephant has one trunk, two ears, and four legs. Two elephants have eight legs. How many legs do five elephants have? ______ legs

5. For one week, Rob and Katie worked for a neighbor. Rob earned $3 a day and Katie earned $4 each day. How much money did they have at the end of seven days?

   ____

Name ______________________________

11-5

Reteach

2MG2.0, 2MG2.1

Sides and Vertices

Chapter Resources

Write how many sides and vertices.

Shape	Sides	Vertices
1. 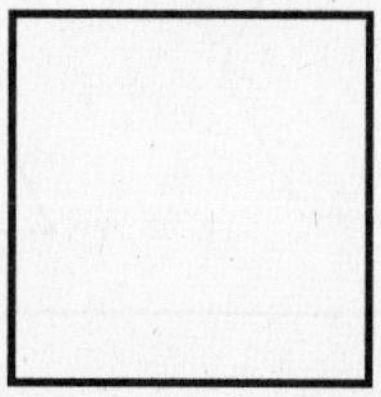		
2. 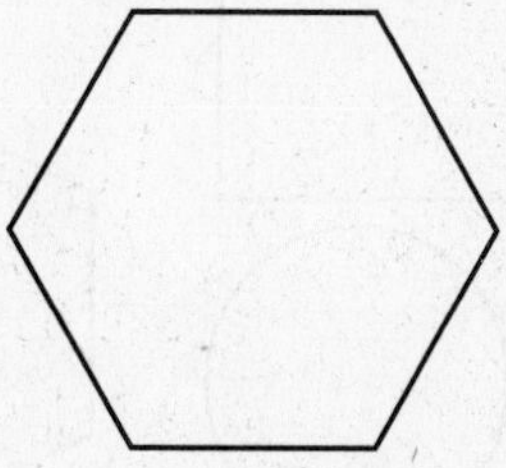		
3. 		
4. 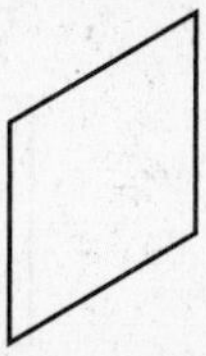		
5. 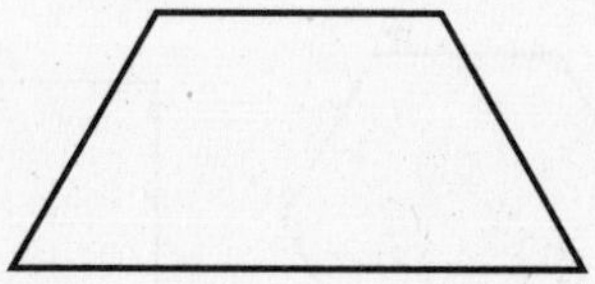		

Name ____________________

11-5

Skills Practice

2MG2.0, 2MG2.1

Sides and Vertices

Preparation: Crayons are needed for this activity.

Read the name of the shape. Color it. Tell how many sides and vertices it has.

1. parallelogram

4 sides

4 vertices

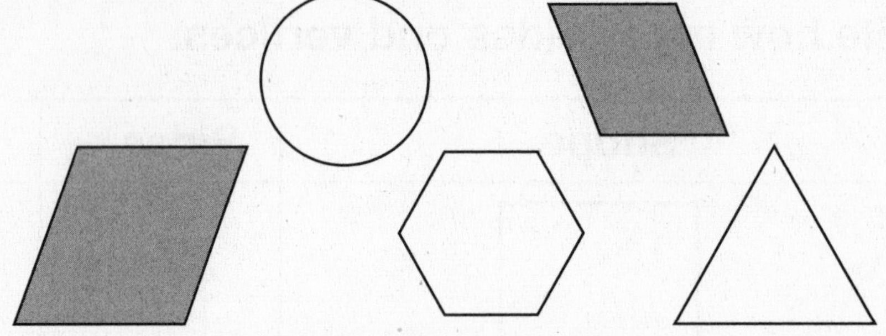

2. trapezoid

_____ sides

_____ vertices

3. circle

_____ sides

_____ vertices

4. hexagon

_____ sides

_____ vertices

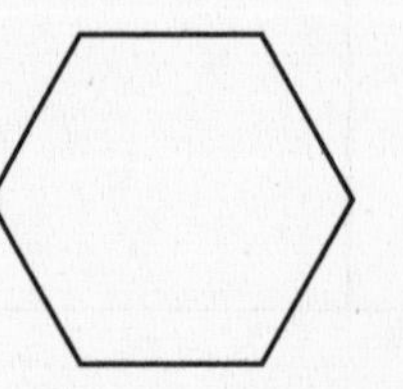
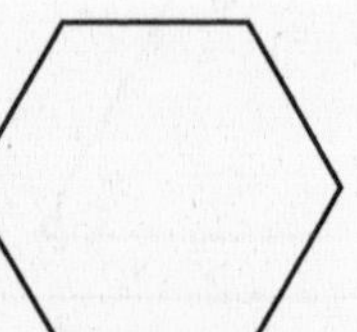
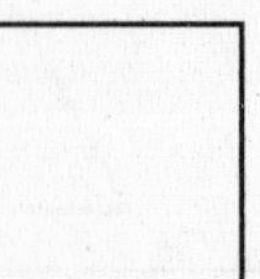

11-6

Name ______________________________

Reteach

2MG2.0, 2MR1.2

Relate Plane Shapes to Solid Shapes

Chapter Resources

You can trace a face of a solid shape to find a plane shape.

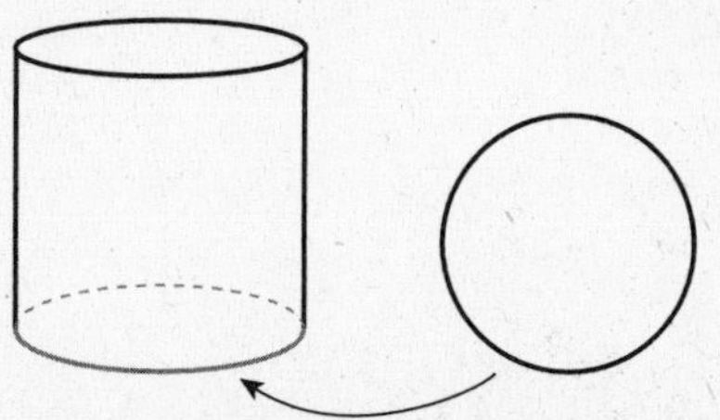

The two faces of the cylinder are circles.

Use solid shapes. Trace around the shaded face shown. Circle the shape you made.

1.	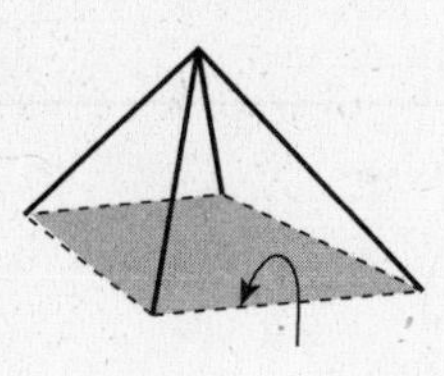	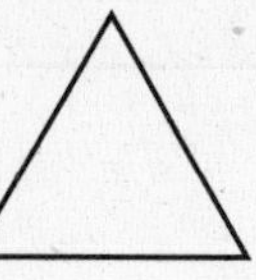
2.	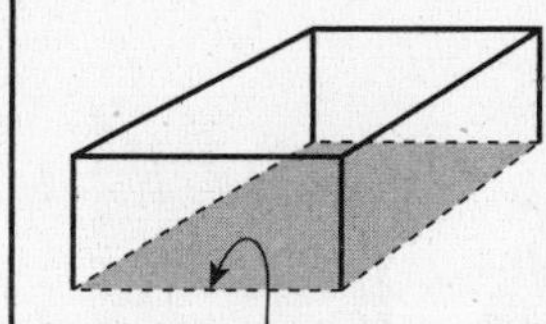	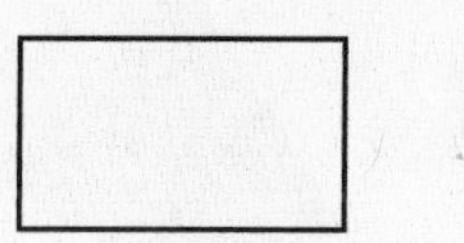
3.	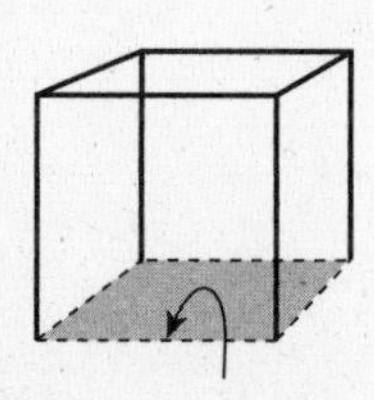	 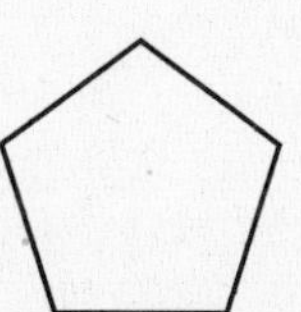 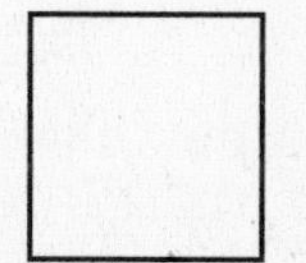
4.	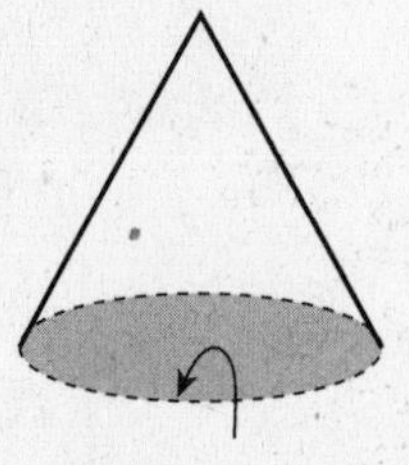	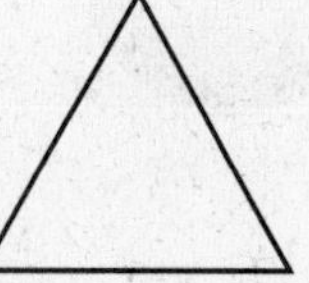 

Name ____________________

11-6

Skills Practice

2MG2.0, 2MR1.2

Relate Plane Shapes to Solid Shapes

Look at the plane shape in each problem. Circle the solid shape you could use to trace it.

1.

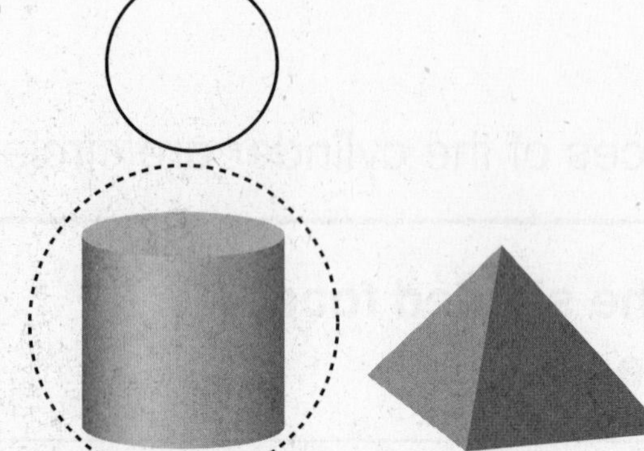

2.

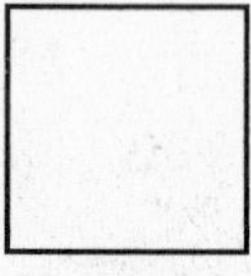

3.

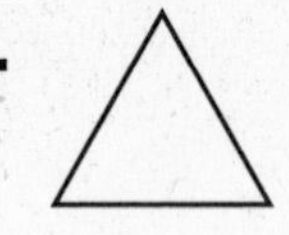

4.

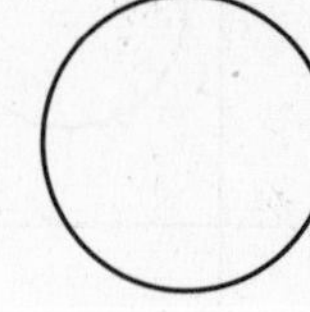

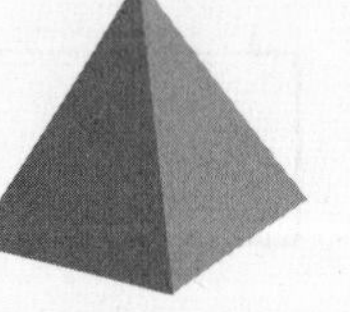

5.

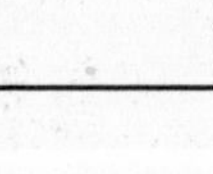

6.

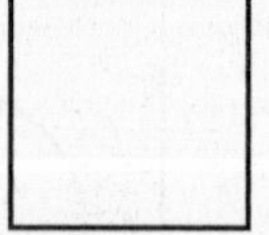

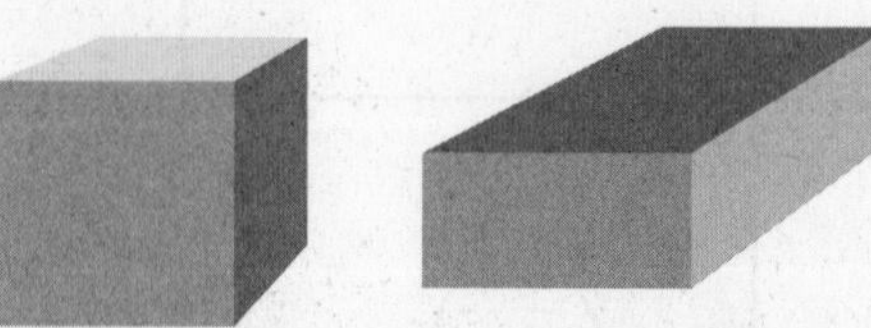

Name ______________________________

11-7

Reteach

2MG2.2, 2MR1.2

Make New Shapes

Preparation: Pattern blocks would be helpful for this activity.

Use △ and □ to make new shapes.

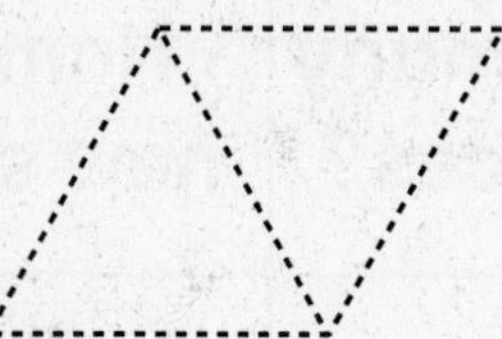

2 triangles can make a parallelogram
4 sides 4 vertices

2 squares can make a rectangle
4 sides 4 vertices

Use triangles to make more new shapes.

1. Make a trapezoid.

Draw the new shape.	How many sides?	How many vertices?

2. Make a hexagon.

Draw the new shape.	How many sides?	How many vertices?

Name ________________________________

11-7

Skills Practice

2MG2.2, 2MR1.2

Make New Shapes

Use pattern blocks to make new shapes.
Complete the chart.

Pattern Blocks	New Shape	How many sides?	How many vertices?	Name of new shape
1. 		6	6	hexagon
2. 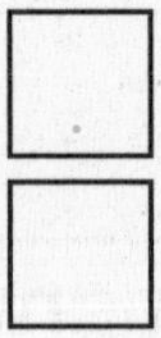		______	______	
3. 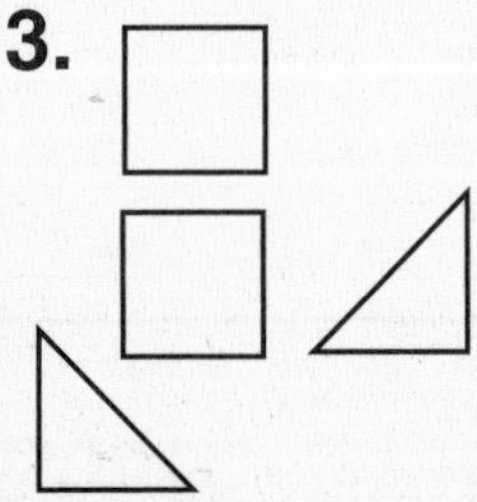		______	______	

Solve. Use pattern blocks to help.

4. How many trapezoids do you need to make a hexagon?

______ trapezoids

5. Make a rectangle from two squares. Then find how many squares do you need to make a bigger square. ______ squares

Name ______________________________

11-8

Reteach (1)

2MG2.0, 2MR2.2

Problem-Solving Investigation: Choose a Strategy

Chapter Resources

Mia has a block. It is a plane shape.
It has 6 sides. Each side is the same length.
Which block does Mia have?

Step 1
Understand

What do I know?

Mia has a plane shape.

The shape has 6 equal sides.

What do I need to find?

What shape it is.

Step 2
Plan

How will I find out the shape?

I can guess and check. This way, I can tell what I think it is and then check my answer.

Step 3
Solve

Guess and check.

The hexagon has 6 equal sides.

Step 4
Check

Look back.

Does my answer make sense? yes

How can I check my answer?

Name ______________________________

11-8

Reteach (2)

2MG2.0, 2MR2.2

Problem-Solving Investigation: Choose a Strategy

Choose a strategy to solve.

Problem-Solving Strategies
- Draw a Picture
- Act It Out
- Guess and Check

1. Lau has to design a robot for class using solid shapes with 6 sides. What shapes could he use?

____

2. Fran's mom gives her an object with 2 faces shaped like circles. Is the object a cake or a party hat? Explain your answer.

____

____

____

3. Two numbers have a sum of 12 and a product of 35. What are the numbers? ______ and ______

4. Toby cuts two triangles out of paper. What is one shape he can make with them?

____

5. Jan makes a shape out of cardboard. It has 6 faces. Some faces are longer than others. It has 12 edges and 8 vertices. What shape has she made?

____

6. Two numbers have a difference of 2 and a sum of 16. What are the numbers?

______ and ______

Name ______________________________

11-8

Skills Practice

2MG2.0, 2MR2.2

Problem-Solving Investigation: Choose a Strategy

Chapter Resources

Choose a strategy to solve.

Problem-Solving Strategies
• Draw a Picture
• Act It Out
• Guess and Check

1. You have 5 coins that total 72¢. What coins do you have?

____

____

2. Jeff says he wants to draw a cube. How many faces and vertices will he have to draw?

_____ faces and _____ vertices

3. Mr. Green told his class to draw a pattern using 3 shapes.

Meg made this pattern: 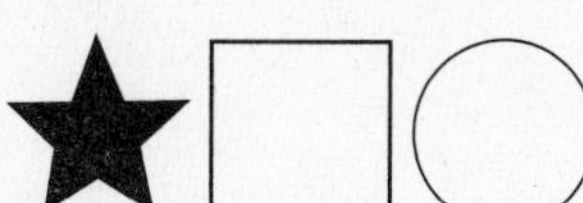

Is there a pattern? _____
Draw a pattern with Meg's shapes.

4. Two numbers have a difference of three and a product of 40. What are the numbers?

_____ and _____

5. I have two faces. I also have no edges or vertices. What shape am I?

____

12-1

Name ____________________

Reteach

2NS6.1, 2MG1.1

Nonstandard Units

Chapter Resources

Preparation: Connecting cubes and paper clips are needed for this activity.

Different units make different measurements.
A ▢ will give a different measurement than a ⊂⊃
for the same object.

Estimate. Then use ▢ and ⊂⊃ to measure.

1. 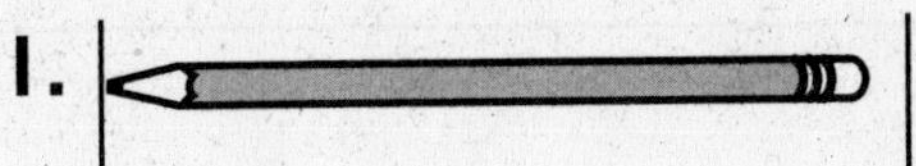

about ______ ▢ measure __________ ▢

about ______ ⊂⊃ measure ______ ⊂⊃

2. 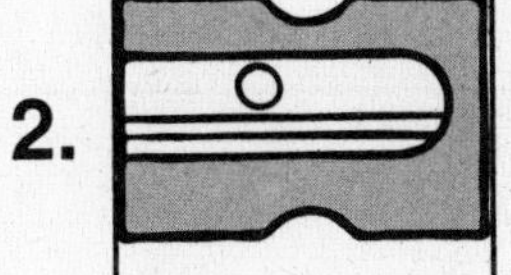

about ______ ▢ measure ______ ▢

about ______ ⊂⊃ measure ______ ⊂⊃

3. 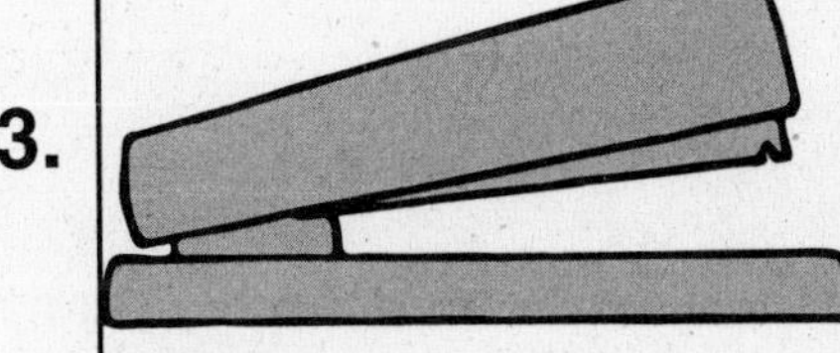

about ______ ▢ measure __________ ▢

about ______ ⊂⊃ measure ______ ⊂⊃

Name ______________________________

12-1

Skills Practice

2NS6.1, 2MG1.2

Nonstandard Units

Preparation: Connecting cubes and paper clips are needed for this activity.

Find the object. Estimate. Then use [paper clip] to measure.

1.

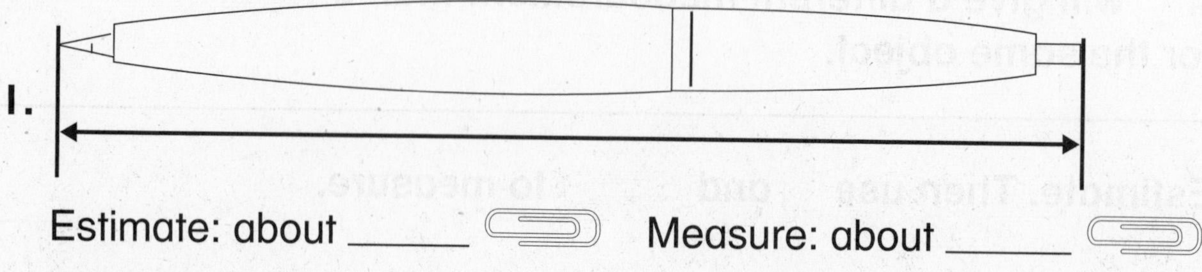

Estimate: about ______ [paper clip] Measure: about ______ [paper clip]

2.

Estimate: about ______ [paper clip] Measure: about ______ [paper clip]

Solve.

3. Jim wants to measure his marker with cubes and paper clips. About how many of each unit?

about ______ [cube] about ______ [paper clip]

Are your answers the same or different? Explain why.

____

____

12-2

Name ___________________________

Reteach

2MG1.3, 2NS6.1

Measure to the Nearest Inch

Chapter Resources

Use an inch ruler to measure length.

Line up the zero end of the ruler with one end of the pencil. Read the number at the other end of the pencil.

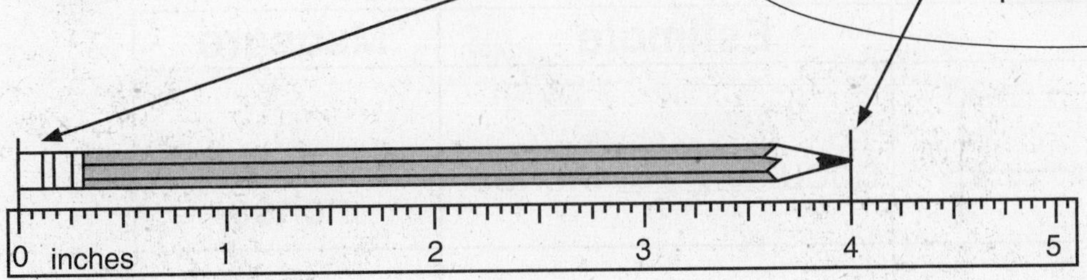

Estimate: about ______ inches   Measure: about ______ inches

Estimate the length of each picture below. Then use an inch ruler to measure.

Picture	Estimate	Measure
1. blue crayon	about _____ inches	about _____ inches
2. paper clip	about _____ inches	about _____ inches
3. eraser	about _____ inches	about _____ inches
4. chalk	about _____ inches	about _____ inches
5. stapler	about _____ inches	about _____ inches

12-2

Name ____________________

Skills Practice

2MG1.3, 2NS6.1

Measure to the Nearest Inch

Find the object. Estimate.
Then use an inch ruler to measure.

Find	Estimate	Measure
1.	about ______ inches	______ inches
2.	about ______ inches	______ inches
3.	about ______ inches	______ inches

Solve.

4. Ali makes a row of 75¢ in quarters. Each quarter is about one inch long. About how long is Ali's row of quarters? Tell how you know. The row is about ______ inches long.

____

____

____

5. Lu measured one [ten-rod]. It was about 4 inches. She put 3 [ten-rods] end to end. About how long was the line of three [ten-rods]? Tell how you know.

The line is about ______ inches long.

____

Name ______________________

12-3

Reteach

2MG1.0, 2NS6.1

Inch, Foot, Yard

Chapter Resources

You can measure with inches, feet, and yards.
A yardstick helps measure larger objects.

About how tall is the desk? Circle the best estimate.

about 12 inches

about 1 yard

Think of the real object. Then circle the best estimate.

1 foot = 12 inches
1 yard = 3 feet

1. 

about 5 inches

about 2 feet

2. 

about 24 inches

about 7 inches

3. 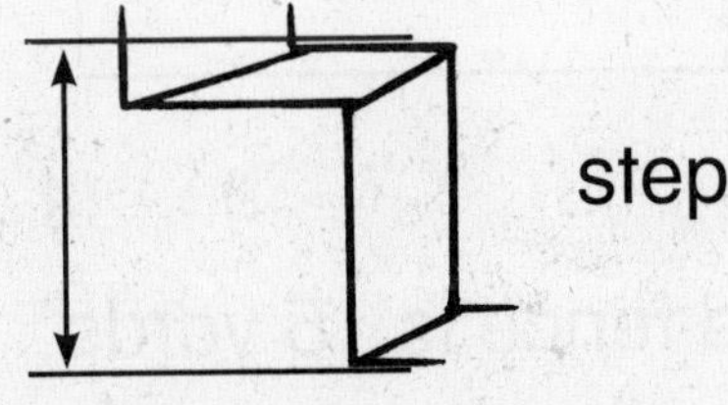

step

about 7 inches

about 1 foot

4. 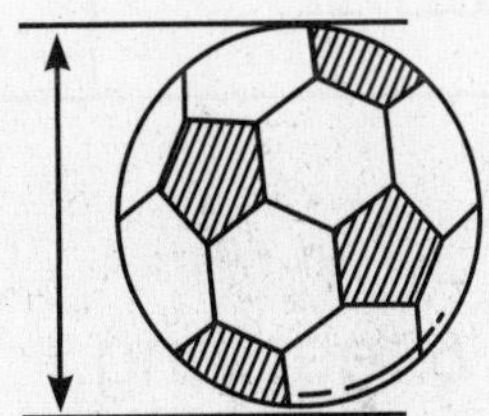

about 9 inches

about 18 inches

12-3

Name ___

Skills Practice

2MG1.0, 2MR2.2

Inch, Foot, Yard

Preparation: An inch ruler and yardstick are needed for this activity.

Find the object. Use inches, feet, or yards.
Estimate. Measure each object in the unit shown.

Find	Estimate	Measure
1.	___ inch	___ inch
2.	___ feet	___ feet
3.	___ inches	___ inches
4.	___ yard	___ yard

Solve.

5. Lita's scarf is 6 feet long. Jill's scarf is 2 feet shorter. How long is Jill's scarf?

___ feet long

6. A wood fence is 15 yards long. An iron fence is 6 yards longer. How long is the iron fence? ___ yards long

Name ______________________________

12-4

Reteach (1)

2MG1.0, 2MR2.2

Problem-Solving Strategy: Use Logical Reasoning

Chapter Resources

Will's family has these three heights:

6 feet 5 feet 4 feet

Will is the shortest.

Will's dad is 2 feet taller than Will.

How tall is Will's sister?

Step 1 **Understand**	**What do I know?** Will is the shortest. Will's dad is 2 feet taller than Will. **What do I need to find out?** How tall is Will's sister?
Step 2 **Plan**	**How will I find out?** I can use logical reasoning. I will use small steps to solve the problem.
Step 3 **Solve**	**Carry out your plan.** Will is shortest, so he must be 4 feet tall. Will's dad is 2 feet taller than Will, so he must be 6 feet tall. One height is left: 5 feet. Will's sister must be 5 feet tall.
Step 4 **Check**	**Look back.** Does my answer make sense?

Name ______________________

12-4

Reteach (2)

2MG1.0, 2MR2.2

Problem-Solving Strategy: Use Logical Reasoning

Use logical reasoning to solve. **Show your work here.**

1. Rita, Anne, and Mei are in a jumping contest. They jump 2 feet, 4 feet, and 1 yard. Rita's jump is measured in yards. Mei jumped farther than Anne. How far did Mei jump?

   ______ feet

2. Pablo, Vince, and Jackson have pictures on the art wall at school. Each picture has a different length: 6 inches, 1 foot, and 1 yard. Vince's picture is the shortest. Pablo's picture is 6 inches longer than Vince's picture. Jackson's picture must be

   __________ long.

3. Coach Jan records how far three students swim: 3 yards, 7 feet, 1 yard. Cam swims 3 times as far as 1 yard. Trey's swim is measured in feet. How far does Val swim?

   ____

12-4

Name ______________________________

Skills Practice

2MG1.0, 2MR2.2

Problem-Solving Strategy: Use Logical Reasoning

Use logical reasoning to solve. **Show your work here.**

1. Diane, Cindy, and Yoko have school photos in these sizes: 1 inch, 6 inches, and 11 inches. Yoko's photo is 5 inches shorter than Cindy's. Diane's photo is not the shortest. How tall is Diane's photo?

   _____ inches

2. The zookeeper measures the baby tiger, elephant, and whale. Their lengths are 5 feet, 1 yard, and 4 feet. The baby tiger is shorter than the baby elephant. The longest baby does not live on land. How long is the baby elephant?

   _____ feet

3. Juan reads that three towns have 3, 7, and 13 inches of snow. West Town has less snow than Rossville. Rossville has ten inches more than Medford. How many inches does West Town have?

   _____ inches

Name ____________________

12-5

Reteach

2MG1.3, 2MR2.2

Measure to the Nearest Centimeter

Chapter Resources

Use the centimeter ruler to measure.

Line up the zero end of the ruler with one end of the crayon. Read the number at the other end of the crayon.

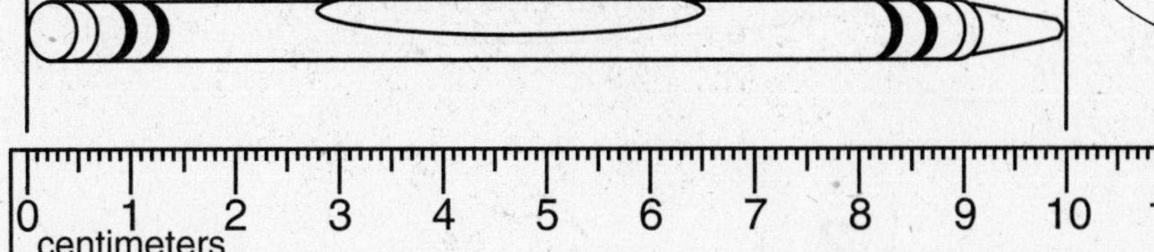

The crayon is about __10__ centimeters long

Write how many centimeters.

1. __6__ centimeters

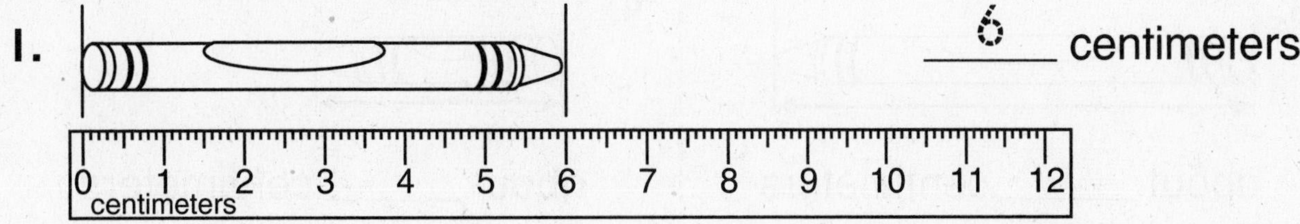

2. ______ centimeters

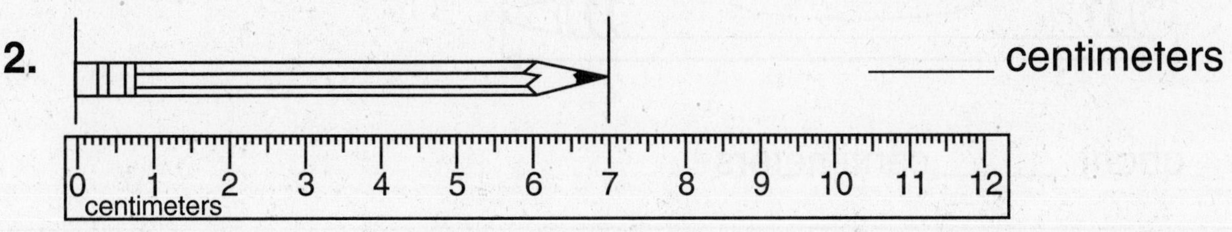

3. ______ centimeters

4. ______ centimeters

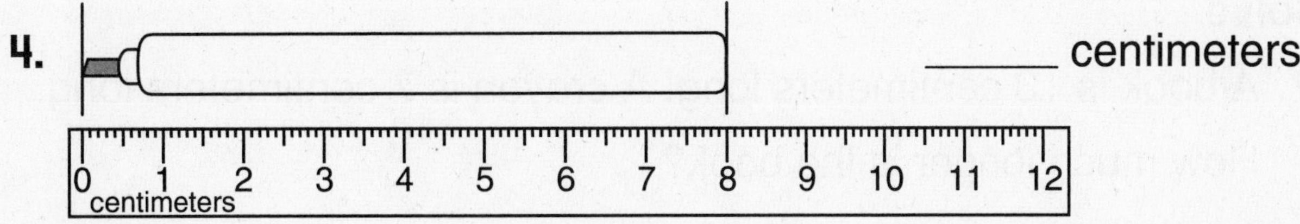

Name ______________________________

12-5

Skills Practice

2MG1.3, 2MR2.2

Measure to the Nearest Centimeter

Preparation: A centimeter ruler is needed for this activity.

Use a centimeter ruler to measure.

Line up the zero end of the ruler with one end of the crayon. Read the number at the other end of the crayon.

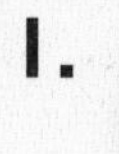

1. 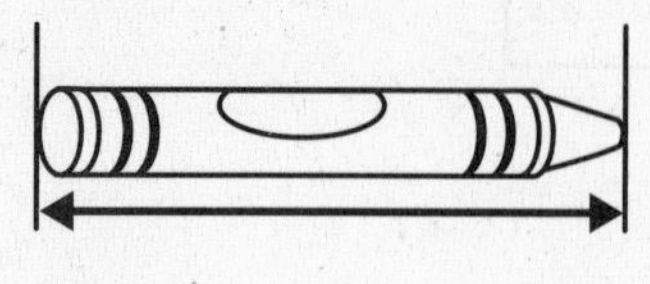

about ______ centimeters

2. 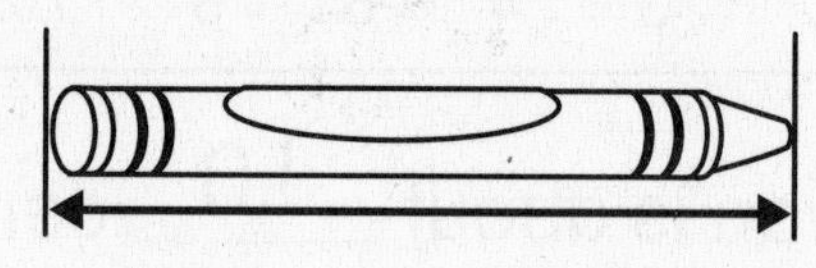

about ______ centimeters

3. 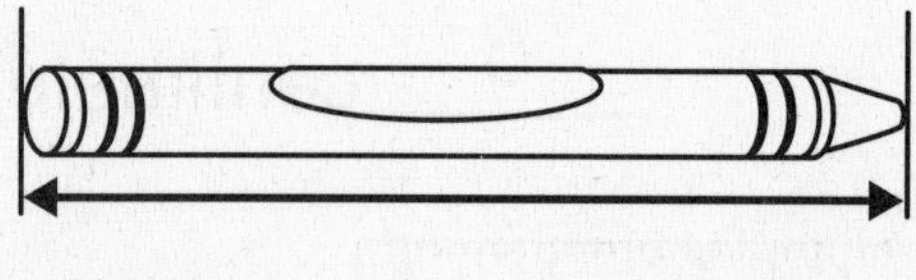

about ______ centimeters

4. 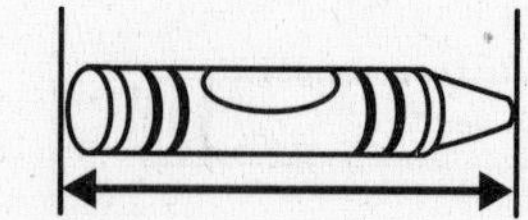

about ______ centimeters

5. 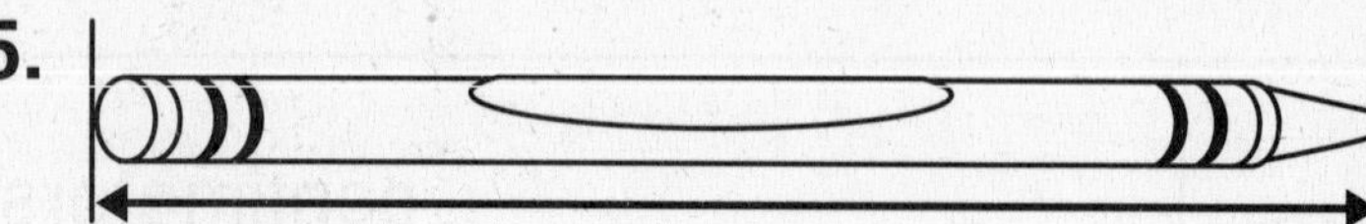

about ______ centimeters

6. 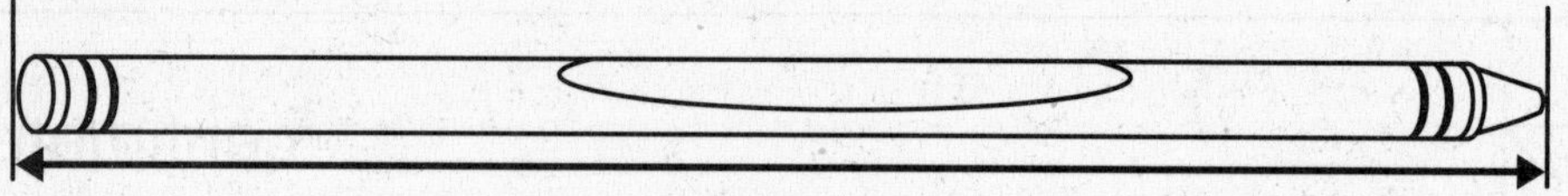

about ______ centimeters

Solve.

7. A book is 13 centimeters long. A crayon is 7 centimeters long. How much longer is the book?

The book is ______ centimeters longer.

12-6

Name ___________________________

Reteach

2NS6.1, 2MG1.1

Centimeter and Meter

Preparation: A centimeter ruler and meter stick are needed for this activity.

Use a meter stick to measure the length of larger objects.

1 meter = 100 centimeters

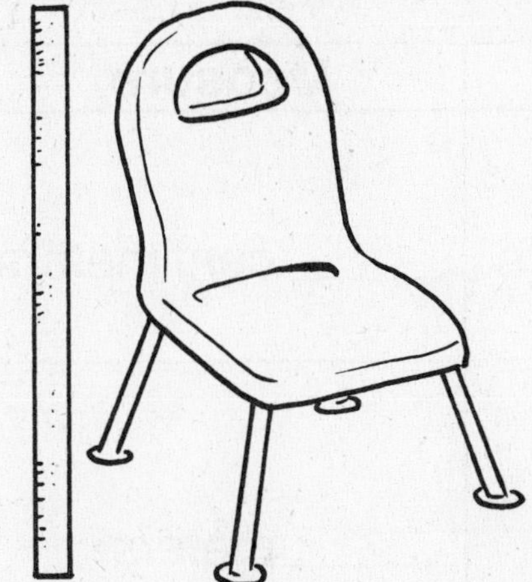

estimate about __1__ meter

measure about __1__ meter

Estimate. Find an object for each length.

Estimate	Object	Measure
1. about 10 centimeters	______ ______	______ centimeters
2. about 20 centimeters	______ ______	______ centimeters
3. about 3 meters	______ ______	______ meters
4. about 1 meter	______ ______	______ meters

Chapter Resources

Name ______________________________

12-6

Skills Practice

2NS6.1, 2MG1.1

Centimeter and Meter

Preparation: A centimeter ruler and meter stick are needed for this activity.

Find the object. Use centimeters or meters.
Estimate. Measure each object in the unit shown.

Find	Estimate	Measure
1.	______ centimeters	______ centimeters
2.	______ meters	______ meters
3.	______ centimeters	______ centimeters
4.	______ meters	______ meters

5. Name three things in your classroom that are longer than 25 centimeters but shorter than a meter. Use a meter stick to measure them.

____

6. Name two things in your classroom that are longer than a meter. Use a meter stick to measure them.

Name ______________________

12-7

Reteach

2MG1.4, 2MR1.2

Time to the Quarter Hour

Chapter Resources

There are 15 minutes in one quarter hour.
Count by fives to find time to the quarter hour.

2:15

15 minutes after two

2:15

2:30

30 minutes after two

___ : ___

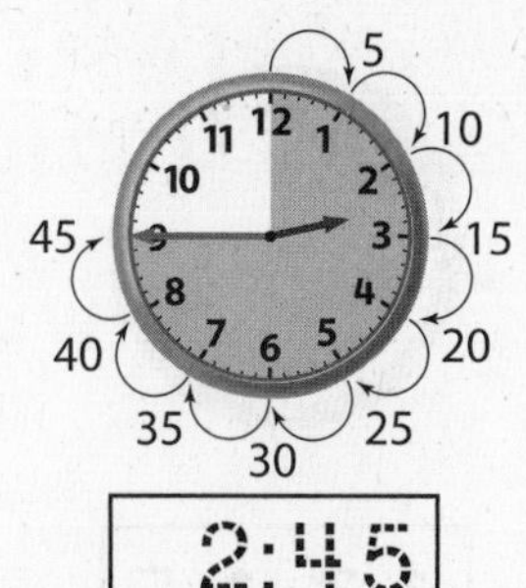

2:45

45 minutes after two

___ : ___

Write the time to the quarter hour.

1.

11:15

___ : ___

___ : ___

2.

___ : ___

___ : ___

___ : ___

3.

___ : ___

___ : ___

___ : ___

Name ______________________________

12-7

Skills Practice

2MG1.4, 2MR1.2

Time to the Quarter Hour

Use your clock. Draw the minute hand to show the time.

1.

12:15

12:30

12:45

2.

8:00

8:15

8:30

3.

2:15

2:30

2:45

Use a pattern to solve.

4. Stu hears the class bell ring at 10:00, 10:15, and 10:30. At what time will the bell ring next? ________

5. A clock tower chimes every quarter hour. Abby hears the chime at 3:30 and at 3:45. When will the clock chime next?

____

Name ___

12-8

Reteach

2MR1.1, 2MR2.0

Problem-Solving Investigation: Choose a Strategy

Chapter Resources

Kim buys 4 yards of animal stickers. Each sticker is 2 inches long. How many stickers does Kim buy?

Step 1
Understand

What do you know?

- Kim buys 4 yards of stickers.
- One sticker is 2 inches long.

What do you need to find?

- How many stickers are in ___ yards.

Step 2
Plan

Make a plan.

Find the number of stickers in one foot. Then make a table to show the number of stickers in 3 feet or ___ yard.

Then, a table can tell the number of stickers in ___ yards.

Step 3
Solve

There are $12 \div 2 = 6$ stickers in one foot.

feet	3	6	9	12
yards	1	___	___	___
stickers	18	36	54	72

This means there are 72 stickers in 4 yards.

Step 4
Check

Look back.

Check to see if your solution is reasonable.
Read the problem again.

Does your table answer the question? yes no

Name ______________________________

12-8

Reteach (2)

2MR1.1, 2MR2.0

Problem-Solving Investigation: Choose a Strategy

Solve. Show your work.

1. Ms. Jones needs 12 yards of ribbon for the class party. One roll of ribbon is 3 yards long. How many rolls does Ms. Jones need?

   ______ rolls

rolls				
yards of ribbon				

2. Mr. Karr is a baker. He finishes a batch of bagels every 15 minutes. His first batch is done at 8:30. He bakes 8 batches. What time is he done?

   ______

3. Vic and his dad are at the park at 4:15. The park is 15 minutes from the theater. They want to see a movie at 5:45. How long can Vic and his dad stay at the park?

   _____ hour _____ minutes

4. Mary's mom is painting her bedroom wall. About one can of paint covers a wall 3 yards high and 4 yards long. Mary's wall is 8 feet high and 11 feet long. Is one can of paint is enough? Explain.

   ____

   ____

12-8

Name ______________________________

Skills Practice

2MR2.0, 2AF1.0

Problem-Solving Investigation: Choose a Strategy

Solve.

1. A

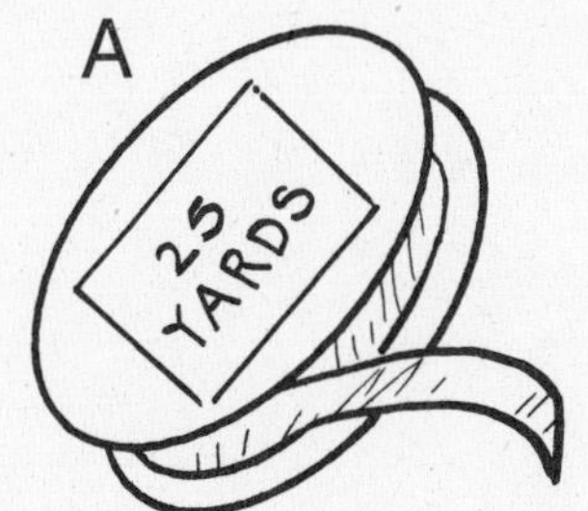

B

66
FEET

C

Kate wants to buy a spool of ribbon. Which spool has the most ribbon?

Spool ______ has the most ribbon

2. Jamal draws a picture 20 inches long and 20 inches wide. He wants to put a ribbon border on it. About how many yards of ribbon does he need? (Hint: Remember, there are 4 sides to a picture).

______ yard(s)

3. Coach Meg's watch beeps every quarter hour. It is 1:00 and her watch is beeping. What are the next 3 times her watch will beep?

______, ______, ______

4. Tim measures his shoe. It is 6 inches long. Then, he walks across a room. He puts the heel of his right shoe against the toe of the left shoe. He says the room is about 20 shoes long. About how long is the room in feet?

about ______ feet

Chapter Resources

Name ______________________

2MG1.5, 2MR1.2

Reteach

Elapsed Time

Count forward to see how much time has gone by.

start time 3 : 00

end time 5 : 00

time 2 hours gone by.

1.

start time ____ : ____

end time ____ : ____

time ______ hour gone by.

2.

start time ____ : ____

end time ____ : ____

time ______ hours gone by.

3.

start time ____ : ____

end time ____ : ____

time ______ hours gone by.

12-9

Name ______________________________

Skills Practice

2MG1.5, 2MR1.2

Elapsed Time

Write each start time and end time.
Then write how much time as passed.

Activity	Start Time	End Time	How long does it take?
1. Go to Grandma's	___ : ___	___ : ___	______ hours
2. Movie	___ : ___	___ : ___	______ hours
3. Skating	___ : ___	___ : ___	______ hour

Solve. Draw the clock hands to show the time.

4. Anna spends 1 hour doing homework. She starts at 6:30. At what time will she finish her homework?

______

5. Steve plays in a basketball game that takes 2 hours. The game starts at 7:15. At what time will the game finish?

______

Name ______________________________

12-10

Reteach

Time Relationships

2MG1.4

Preparation: Scissors and glue are needed for this activity.

Use real life examples to help estimate time.

How long does a bath take?

15 (minutes)

hours

A 15-hour bath **is not** realistic. A 15-minute bath **is** realistic.

Cut out the time units below. Glue the correct time units to solve.

1. cook dinner

45 ______________________

2.

play soccer

1 ______________________

seconds	minutes	hours
days	weeks	months

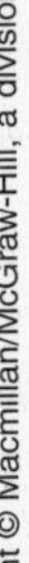

Name ______________________________

12-10

Skills Practice

2MG1.4

Time Relationships

1 minute = 60 seconds	1 week = 7 days
1 hour = 60 minutes	1 month = 4 weeks
1 day = 24 hours	1 year = 12 months or 52 weeks

Circle the best unit to measure the time for each event.

1. to play a game

minutes days

2. to wash your face

minutes hours

3. to write your name

months minutes

4. to watch a movie

minutes hours

Solve.

5. Andy and his mom are making noodles. Their directions are torn. How long should they cook the noodles?

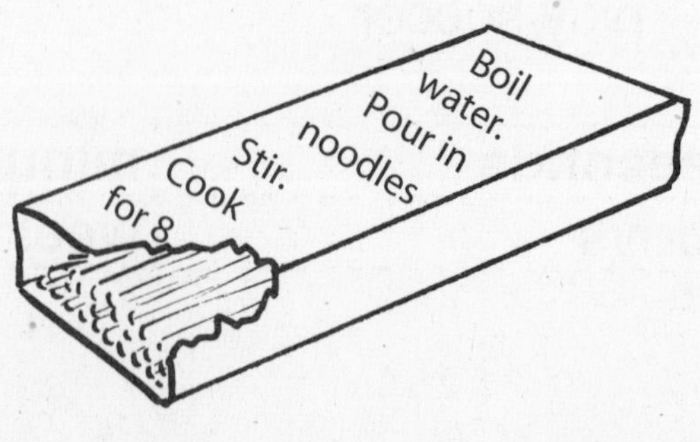

8 ______________

13-1

Name ____________________

Reteach

2NS2.2, 2AF1.0

Add Hundreds

Chapter Resources

Preparation: Hundred cubes are needed for this activity.

Using a model can help add hundreds.

200 + 300 = ?

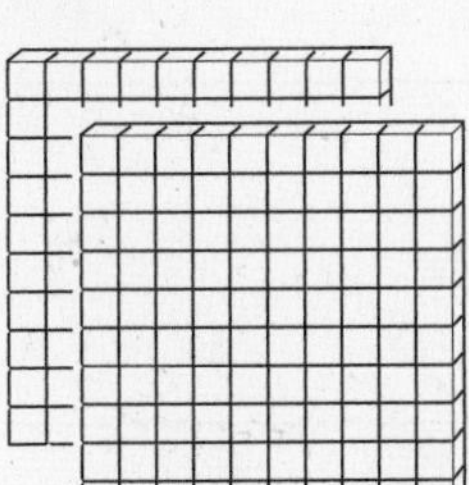

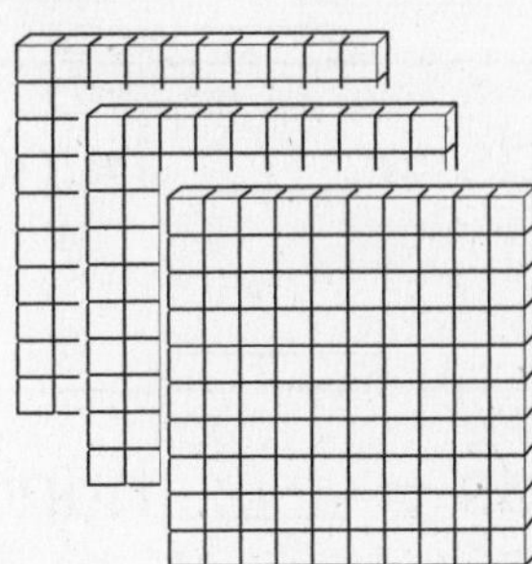

count: 100, 200 count on: 300, 400, 500

200 + 300 = 500

Use hundred cubes to model each problem.
Write your answer.

1. 100 + 200 = _____

---

2. 100 + 300 = _____

3. 200 + 200 = _____

4. 100 + 100 = _____

5. 200 + 300 = _____

6. 200 + 100 = _____

7. 400 + 100 = _____

Name ___________________________

13-1

Skills Practice

2NS2.2, 2AF1.0

Add Hundreds

Add.

1. 4 hundreds + 2 hundreds = _____ hundreds

   400 + 200 = _____

2. 3 hundreds + 3 hundreds = _____ hundreds

   300 + 300 = _____

3. 5 hundreds + 4 hundreds = _____ hundreds

   500 + 400 = _____

4.

200	500	400	700	400
+ 100	+ 200	+ 300	+ 100	+ 200

Solve.

5. Kal has 400 pennies. His sister also has 400 pennies. How many pennies do they have in all?

   _____ hundreds + _____ hundreds = _____ hundreds

   400 + 400 = _____ pennies

6. Joy has 300 stickers. Juan has 500 stickers. How many total stickers are there? Write a number sentence to solve.

   _____ hundreds + _____ hundreds = _____ hundreds

   _____ + _____ = _____ stickers

Name ______________________________

13-2

Reteach

Regroup Ones

Preparation: Base-ten blocks are needed for this activity.

You can use cubes to model regrouping.

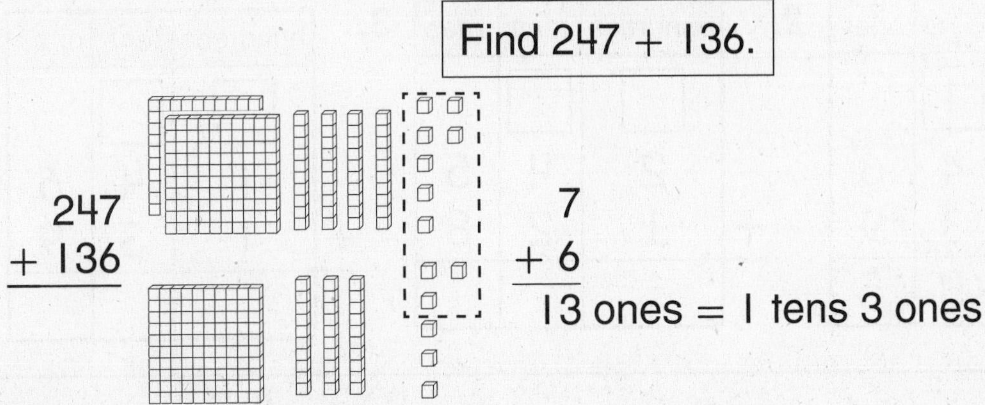

Regroup the ones.
Then add the tens and hundreds.

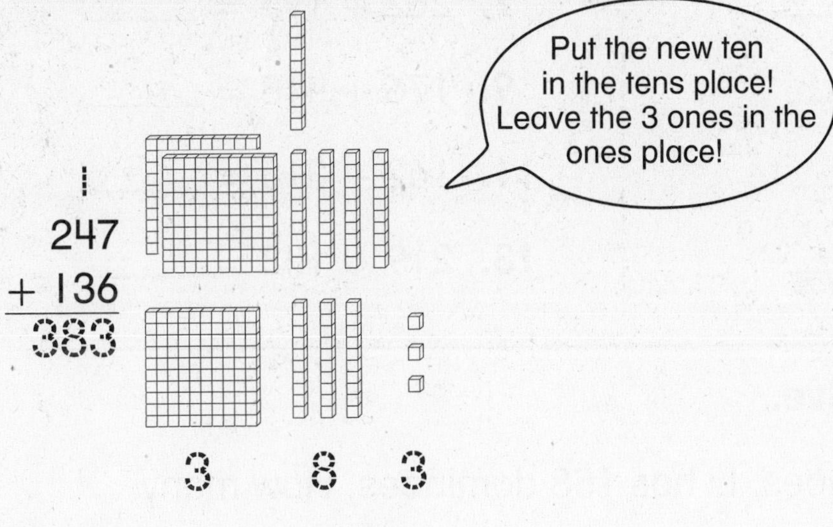

So, 247 + 136 = 383

Use cubes to model each problem. Regroup blocks to solve.

1. 129 + 203 = _____

2. 262 + 119 = _____

3. 288 + 306 = _____

4. 469 + 228 = _____

13-2

Name ____________________

Skills Practice

2NS2.2, 2AF1.2

Regroup Ones

Preparation: Base-ten blocks are needed for this activity.

Use [ten rod] to add.

1.

	hundreds	tens	ones
	☐	1	
	1	4	6
+	1	3	9
	2	8	5

2.

	hundreds	tens	ones
	☐	☐	
	2	4	5
+	1	2	8

3.

	hundreds	tens	ones
	☐	☐	
	1	4	6
+	1	3	9

4. 271 + 309 = ______

5. 325 + 106 = ______

6. 183 + 408 = ______

7. 262 + 199 = ______

8. 364 + 317 = ______

9. 176 + 418 = ______

10. 237 + 155 = ______

11. 162 + 318 = ______

12. 308 + 304 = ______

13. 219 + 143 = ______

Use [ten rod] to solve.

14. Ira has 315 dominoes. Li has 158 dominoes. How many dominoes in all?

______ dominoes

15. Jose has 224 marbles. Bess has 357 marbles. How many total marbles?

______ marbles

Name ______________________________

13-3

Reteach

Regroup Tens

If there are 10 or more tens, you need to regroup. A model can help regroup tens.

Find 370 + 290. Draw your models.

Use ☐ for hundreds and | for tens.

370

+ 290

Regroup 10 tens as 1 hundred!

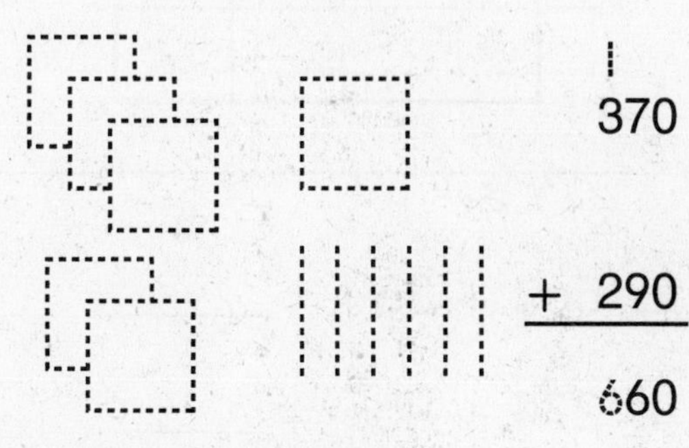

Add these together

So, 370 + 290 = 660

Use ▭ to add.

1. 290 + 350 = ______

2. 120 + 280 = ______

Show your work here.

Name ______________________________

13-3

Skills Practice

2NS2.2, 2MR1.2

Regroup Tens

Preparation: Base-ten blocks are needed for this assessment.

Use [ten-rod] to add.

1.

	hundreds	tens	ones
	1		
	2	7	5
+	2	5	4
	5	2	9

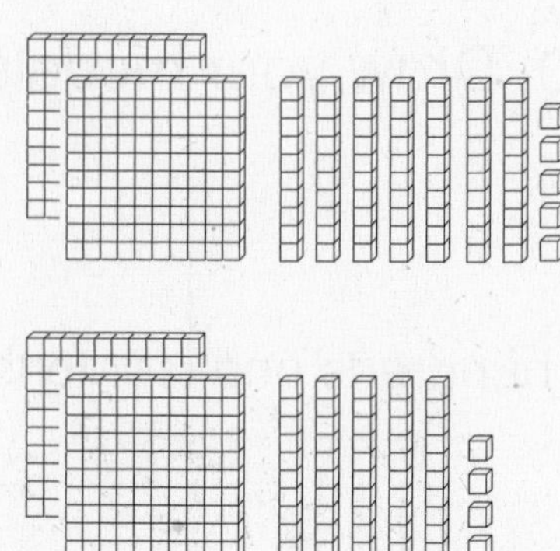

2. 562 + 354 = ______

3. 352 + 493 = ______

4. 274 + 455 = ______

5. 482 + 185 = ______

6. 183 + 471 = ______

7. 282 + 333 = ______

8. 169 + 160 = ______

9. 252 + 451 = ______

Solve. Use [ten-rod], if needed.

10. Kay has 429 rocks in her collection. She finds 390 more. How many rocks does Kay have?

______

11. Luis has 543 baseball cards. His sister has 362. How many ards do they have in all?

______

13-4

Name ______________________________

Reteach (1)

2AF1.3, 2MR1.0

Problem-Solving Strategy: Make a Table

Maya and Tom want to take a class.
Maya has soccer practice until 4:00.
Tom has a piano lesson at 6:00.
Which class can they take?

World Cooking Classes		
Class	**Time Class Starts**	**Time Class Ends**
African Treats	2:00	3:00
French Food	3:00	4:30
Chinese Cooking	4:30	5:00
Mexican Dinners	5:00	7:00

Step 1
Understand

What do I know?

Maya is busy until 4:00.
Tom is busy after 6:00.

What do I need to find out?

Which cooking class they both can take.

Step 2
Plan

How will I find out which class they both can take?

I will find a class that begins after 4:00 for Maya and ends before 6:00 for Tom.

Step 3
Solve

Write down information from the table.

Maya can make the 4:30 and 5:00 classes.

Tom cannot make the 5:00 class.

They can both take Chinese Cooking.

Step 4
Check

Look Back.

How did the table help me to answer the question?

Name ____________________

13-4

Reteach (2)

2AF1.3, 2MR1.0

Problem-Solving Strategy: Make a Table

Use the tables to solve.

1. A storyteller is coming to the library on Saturday. Jack has a swimming lesson until 12:00. Flora wants to hear a story that is an hour long. Which story should Jack and Flora listen to?

Story	Time Story Starts	Time Story Ends
Wolf and the Drum	11:00	12:00
Old Man Winter	12:30	1:00
Tina Races the Tiger	1:00	2:00
Rabbit's New Vest	2:00	2:30

____

2. Andre has $3. Then, he buys a gift for his mom.

a bunch of daisies $1.50
beaded ring $2.00
toy cat 40¢

He has some money left, so he buys the toy cat for his sister. Now Andre has 60¢. What did he buy for his mom?

____

3. Ms. Ling's class is going to the science museum. She made a list of the activities for the day.

Museum Trip	
see space models	9:30–10:30
see movie: On the Moon	10:30–12:00
eat lunch	12:00–1:00
See dinosaur bones	1:00–2:00

How long is the movie? ____________________

13-4

Name ______________________

Skills Practice

2AF1.3, 2MR1.0

Problem-Solving Strategy: Make a Table

Chapter Resources

Use the table to answer the questions.

Flights to Seattle from Minneapolis:

Flight Number	Leaves	Arrives
206	7:10 A.M.	1:20 P.M.
305	9:30 A.M.	4:00 P.M.
491	12:50 P.M.	6:50 P.M.
511	6:05 P.M.	12:15 A.M.

1. Paul leaves for Seattle on Flight 305. Tom leaves on Flight 206. How long will Tom arrive before Paul arrives?

____

2. Jane is taking Flight 491 to Seattle. The plane leaves an hour late. What time will the plane arrive in Seattle? __________

3. Three flights will last the same length of time. Which flight is longer than the others? __________

Complete the table to solve.

4. There are 10 people in each raft. How many people are in 5 rafts?

Rafts	1				
People	10				

Name ____________________

13-5

Reteach

2NS2.0, 2NS6.0

Estimate Sums

Chapter Resources

You can estimate to find an answer that is close to the exact answer.

There are 517 people in Cold Creek. There are 281 people in Old Town. About how many people live in the two towns?

Step 1

Look at the tens. Round each addend to the nearest **hundred**.

517 rounds to → 500
+ 281 rounds to → + 300

Step 2

Add the new addends to find the estimated sum.

500
+ 300
800

The number of people in the two towns is about 800.

Round each number to the nearest *hundred*. Estimate each sum.

1. 489 →
+ 311 → +

2. 466 →
+ 195 → +

Round each number to the nearest *ten*. Estimate each sum.

3. 606 →
+ 247 → +

4. 307 →
+ 258 → +

Name ______________________________

13-5

Skills Practice

2NS2.0, 2NS6.0

Estimate Sums

Round each number to the nearest *ten*.
Estimate the sum.

1. 302 → ____
+ 287 → + ____

2. 686 → ____
+ 174 → + ____

3. 365 → ____
+ 209 → + ____

4. 405 → ____
+ 325 → + ____

Round each number to the nearest *hundred*.
Estimate the sum.

5. 518 → ____
+ 169 → + ____

6. 701 → ____
+ 216 → + ____

7. 176 → ____
+ 315 → + ____

8. 390 → ____
+ 412 → + ____

Solve.

9. There are 410 parents and 526 children in the park. Rounding to the nearest hundred, how many people are in the park?

______ people

10. Mr. Tan sells 215 apples on Wednesday and 486 apples on Sunday. Rounding to the nearest ten, how many apples does Mr. Tan sell? ______ apples

Name ____________________

13-6

Reteach

2NS2.2, 2NS5.0

Add Money

Chapter Resources

Line up decimal points to add money.

Jim buys the duck and the dog. How much does he spend?

$$\begin{array}{r} \$1.72 \\ +\ 2.35 \\ \hline \$4.07 \end{array}$$

Add. **Show your work here.**

1. Lee has $5.00. She buys the pig and the cat. How much money does she spend?

2. Sammy buys the duck and the rabbit. How much does he spend?

3. Pam buys the dog and the cat. How much money does she spend?

Name ____________________

13-6

Skills Practice

2NS2.2, 2NS5.0

Add Money

Solve.

1. $2.69 + 3.45

2. $3.75 + 1.41

3. $7.11 + 1.94

4. $3.87 + 0.75

5. $2.91 + 5.01

6. $2.09 + 3.76

7. $0.89 + 5.88

8. $1.25 + 1.95

9. $2.09 + 2.99

Solve.

10. Amy pays $3.11 for a sandwich and juice. She pays another 89 cents for an orange. How much does Amy spend on lunch?

____

11. Mr. Bailey spends $2.11 for pencils. He spends $3.47 for a notebook. If he buys a folder for 50 cents, how much will Mr. Bailey spend?

____

13-7

Name ______________________________

Reteach (1)

2MR1.1, 2NS5.0

Problem-Solving Investigation: Choose a Strategy

Chapter Resources

Mia has $4.87 in her piggy bank. Her sister Tanya has $4.21 in her piggy bank. How much money do the sisters have in all?

Problem-Solving Strategies

- Use Logical Reasoning
- Make a Chart
- Write a Number Sentence

Step 1 **Understand**	**What do I know?** Mia has $4.87. Tanya has $4.21. **What do I need to find out?** How much money altogether?
Step 2 **Plan**	**How will I find out the total?** I can write a number sentence.
Step 3 **Solve**	**Write a number sentence.** + ______ The sisters have ______ altogether.
Step 4 **Check**	**Look back.** I wrote a number sentence. I added to find how much money altogether.

13-7

Name ____

Reteach (2)

2MR1.1, 2NS2.2

Problem-Solving Investigation: Choose a Strategy

Problem-Solving Strategies

- Use Logical Reasoning
- Make a Chart
- Write a Number Sentence

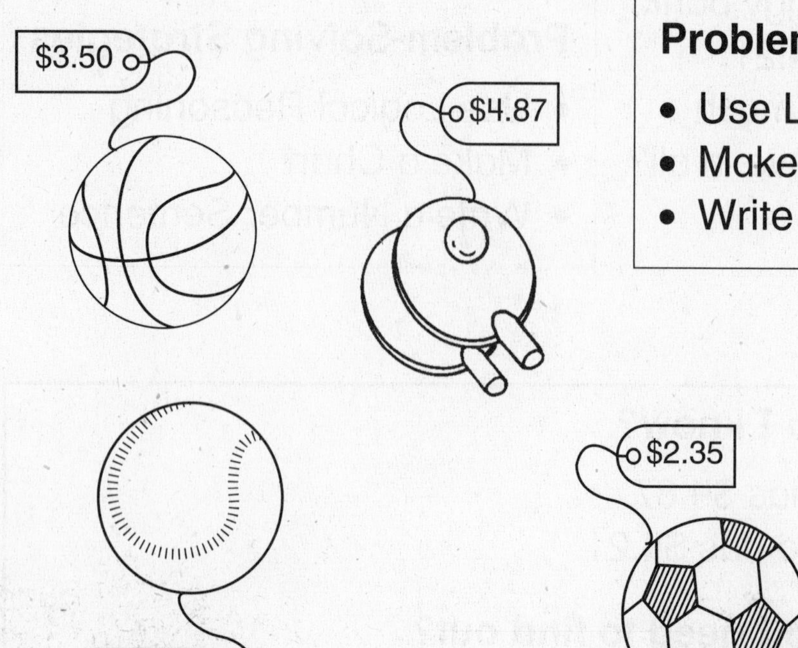

1. Dar wants to buy the basketball and the baseball. How much will he spend in all? ________

2. Lonnie has $7.65. He thinks he has enough money to buy the football and the soccer ball. Is he correct? Explain.

____

3. Name the two most expensive items shown above. What would be the total cost of these two items?

____

4. Josh buys 2 footballs. Jeff buys 3 basketballs. Who spends more?

____

13-7

Name ____________________

Skills Practice

2MR1.1, 2NS2.2

Problem-Solving Investigation: Choose a Strategy

Problem-Solving Strategies

- Use Logical Reasoning
- Make a Chart
- Write a Number Sentence

1. Mrs. Hayes buys her son lunch. Lunch #1 is $3.89. Lunch #2 is $4.19. Lunch #3 is $4.89. Mrs. Hayes orders #2. If her son orders #3, how much will Mrs. Hayes pay?

   ____

2. Dale spends $2.85 on bus tickets. His friend Jay spends $3.60 on bus tickets the same day. How much do the two spend on bus tickets in all?

   ____

3. Pia wants to buy a doll for $4.27. She wants to buy the same doll for her friend. How much money will Pia spend on both dolls?

   ____

4. Sari has 5 dollars. She buys a sandwich for $3.00 and a juice for $1.29. Apples cost $0.89. Does she have enough to buy an apple too?

   ____

14-1

Name ______________________

Reteach

2NS2.2, 2AF1.0

Subtract Hundreds

Chapter Resources

Use subtraction facts to subtract hundreds.

Find 600 – 300.

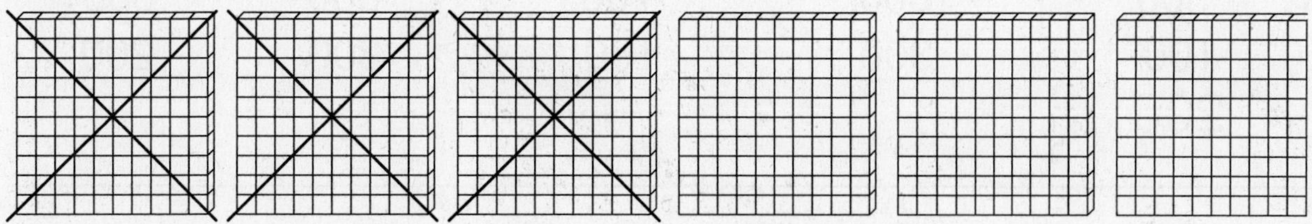

6 hundreds – 3 hundreds = ______ hundreds

600 – 300 = ______

Subtract.

1. 4 hundreds – 1 hundred = ______ hundreds

   400 – 100 = ______

2. 7 hundreds – 3 hundreds = ______ hundreds

   700 – 300 = ______

3. 8 hundreds – 5 hundreds = ______ hundreds

   800 – 500 = ______

4. $\begin{array}{r} 600 \\ -\ 100 \\ \hline \end{array}$ $\quad$ $\begin{array}{r} 500 \\ -\ 200 \\ \hline \end{array}$ $\quad$ $\begin{array}{r} 800 \\ -\ 300 \\ \hline \end{array}$ $\quad$ $\begin{array}{r} 600 \\ -\ 200 \\ \hline \end{array}$ $\quad$ $\begin{array}{r} 500 \\ -\ 100 \\ \hline \end{array}$

Name ______________________________

14-1

Skills Practice

2NS2.2, 2AF1.0

Subtract Hundreds

Subtract.

1. 300 − 100 = 200   800 − 300   700 − 100   600 − 300   600 − 200

1. 300	800	700	600	600
− 100	− 300	− 100	− 300	− 200
200				

2. 400	500	600	800	500
− 100	− 100	− 500	− 100	− 300

3. 500	900	600	700	800
− 200	− 200	− 400	− 400	− 500

Solve.

Show your work here.

4. 900 children are in the park. 700 adults are in the park. How many more children are there than adults?

   ______ more children

5. 800 people see a movie on Friday. 900 people see the movie on Saturday. How many more people go to the movie on Saturday?

   ______ more people

Name ______________________________

14-2

Reteach

2NS2.0, 2AF1.0

Regroup Tens

hundreds	tens	ones
	☐	☐
1	6	3
− 1	3	5

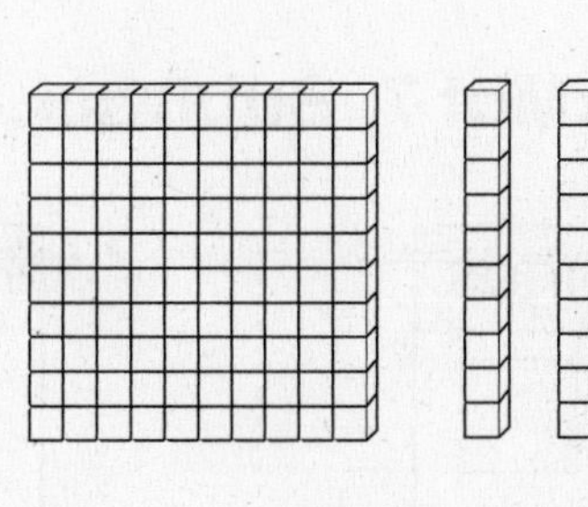

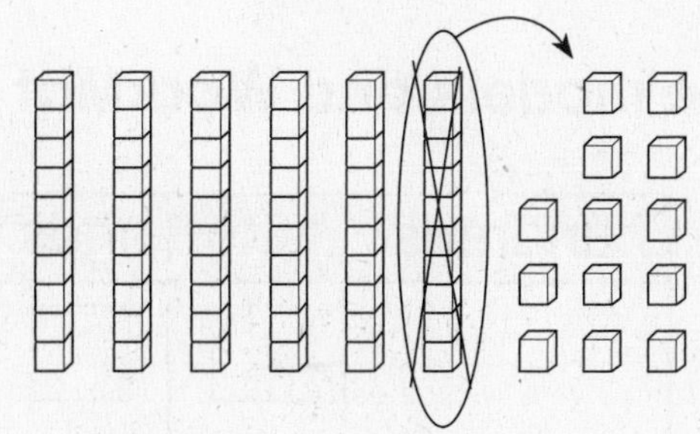

Remember: regroup 1 ten as 10 ones.

Use the models to subtract.

1.

hundreds	tens	ones
	☐	☐
4	3	7
− 2	1	8

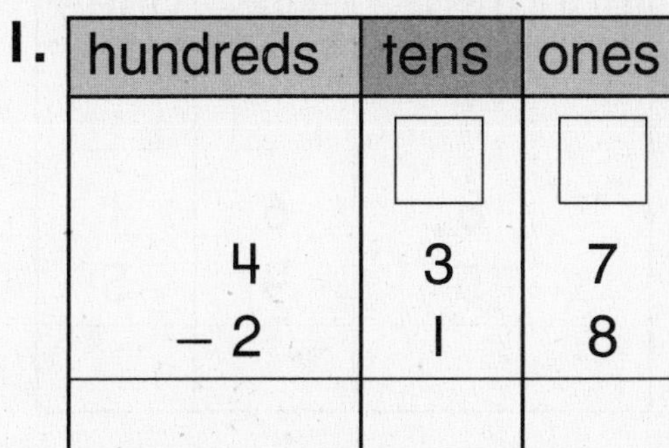

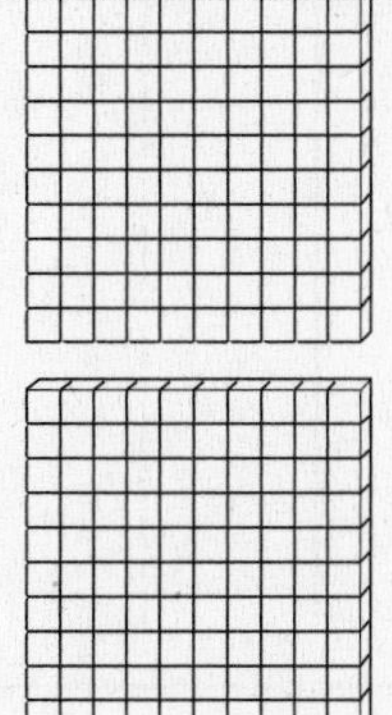

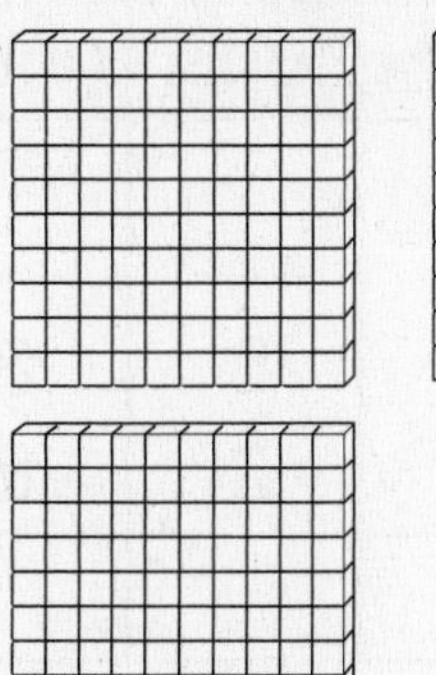

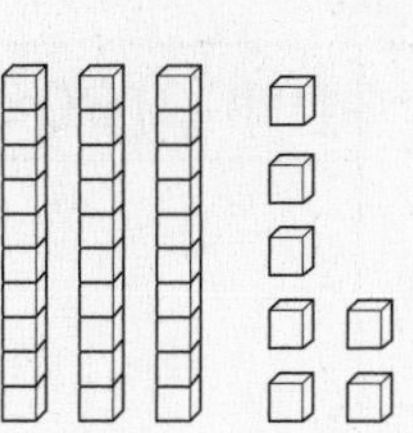

Use models and WorkMat 7. Subtract.

2. 321 − 13 = ______

3. 549 − 211 = ______

4. 869 − 5 = ______

5. 623 − 415 = ______

6. 460 − 152 = ______

7. 708 − 26 = ______

Chapter Resources

Name ______________________________

14-2

Skills Practice

2NS2.0, 2AF1.0

Regroup Tens

Preparation: Base-ten blocks are needed for this activity.

Use models and WorkMat 7. Subtract.

1.

hundreds	tens	ones
	□	□
7	6	3
− 3	2	5

2.

hundreds	tens	ones
	□	□
6	5	7
− 4	2	9

3.

hundreds	tens	ones
	□	□
4	8	3
− 1	2	8

4.

hundreds	tens	ones
	□	□
8	6	1
− 5	4	5

5. 688 − 117 = ______

6. 945 − 538 = ______

7. 573 − 451 = ______

8. 783 − 261 = ______

9. 454 − 344 = ______

10. 857 − 675 = ______

Solve.

11. 377 people see a play on Friday night. 495 people see a play on Saturday. How many more people see the play on Saturday?

______ people

Name ____________________

14-3

Reteach

2NS2.2, 2MR1.2

Regroup Hundreds

Preparation: Base-ten blocks are needed for this activity.

Step 1
Subtract the ones.
Write how many ones are left.

Step 2
Subtract the tens.
Regroup 1 hundred as 10 tens. Write the new number of hundreds and tens in the boxes.

Step 3
Subtract the hundreds.
Write how many hundreds are left.

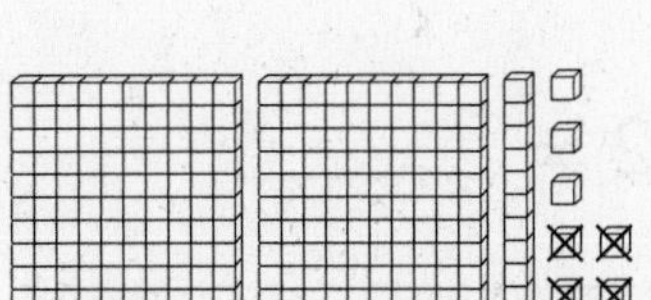

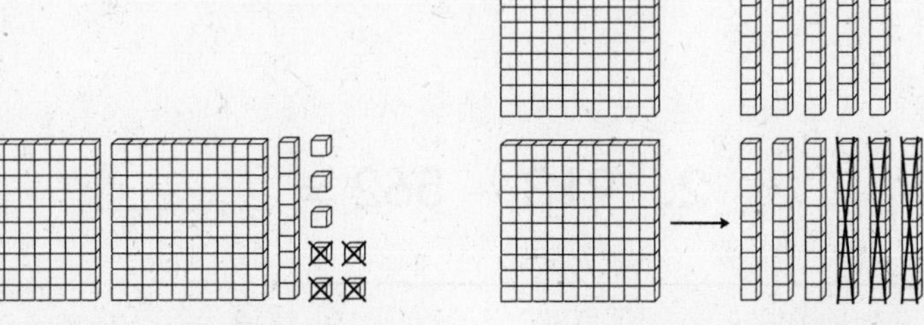

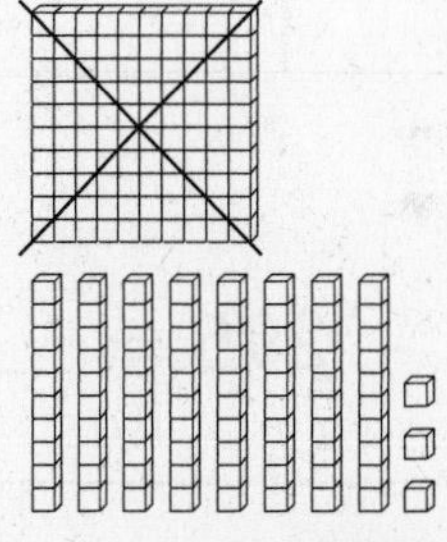

hundreds	tens	ones
☐	☐	
2	1	7
− 1	3	4

hundreds	tens	ones
☐	☐	
2	1	7
− 1	3	4

hundreds	tens	ones
☐	☐	
2	1	7
− 1	3	4

Use models and WorkMat 7. Subtract.

1. 827 − 433 = ______

2. 245 − 153 = ______

3. 597 − 489 = ______

4. 762 − 234 = ______

5. 624 − 325 = ______

6. 943 − 144 = ______

Name ______________________________

14-3

Skills Practice

2NS2.2, 2MR 1.2

Regroup Hundreds

Preparation: Base-ten blocks are needed for this activity.

Use models and WorkMat 7. Subtract.

hundreds	tens	ones
2	12	
3	2	8
− 2	7	7
	5	1

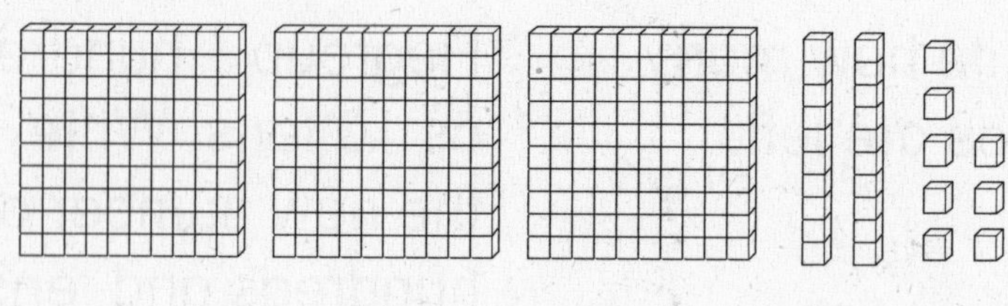

1. 567 − 295 = ______
2. 912 − 562 = ______
3. 727 − 382 = ______
4. 838 − 445 = ______
5. 478 − 416 = ______
6. 648 − 377 = ______
7. 346 − 268 = ______
8. 256 − 131 = ______
9. 871 − 596 = ______
10. 158 − 98 = ______

Solve. Show your work.

11. Penny had 347 pumpkins for sale. She sold 255 pumpkins. How many pumpkins did Penny have left? ______ pumpkins

Name ______________________________

14-4

Reteach (1)

2MR2.2, 2AF1.0

Problem-Solving Strategy: Guess and Check

Chapter Resources

Two squirrels collect the nuts from a walnut tree.
They collect 119 nuts in all.
How many nuts might each of the squirrels collected?

58, 64, 61, 55

Step 1 **Understand**

What do I know?

2 squirrels collected a total of 119 nuts.

What do I need to find out?

How many nuts did each squirrel collect.

Step 2 **Plan**

How will I solve the problem?

I can guess and check to solve.

Step 3 **Solve**

Guess and Check

Use guess and check to solve. 58 + 64 = 122. That is too many nuts. 61 + 55 = 116. That isn't enough nuts. 58 + 61 = 119. That's the answer!

Step 4 **Check**

Look back.

Did I answer the question? Were there any cominations of numbers that could have worked? ______________________________

____

14-4

Name ______________________________

Reteach (2)

2MR2.2, 2AF1.0

Problem-Solving Strategy: Guess and Check

Solve. Circle the correct answers.

1. Jessica and Josh won a total of 68 awards for state talent contests. How many awards might each of them have won?

   23, 45, 15, 54

2. What number am I?
   I am more than 500.
   I have a 7 in the ones place.
   The sum of my three numbers is 15

   547, 735, 447, 627, 555

3. Ben collects stamps with either of his 2 favorite colors in them. He has 55 different stamps. How many and what color might each of the them be?

   30 red, 29 yellow, 25 red, 30 blue

4. Jose, Mick, and Dan helped wash cars on Saturday for their school band. Together, they wash 71 cars. How many cars might each of them wash?

   25, 27, 17, 21, 19

14-4

Name ____________________

Skills Practice

2MR2.2, 2AF1.0

Problem-Solving Strategy: Guess and Check

Solve. Circle the correct answers.

1. What number am I?
   I am more than 250.
   I have a 3 in the ones place.
   The sum of my three numbers is 9.

   443, 603, 153, 702, 523

2. Tonya and Melissa sell 45 rolls of wrapping paper for their holiday fundraiser. How many rolls might each of them have sold?

   17, 19, 30, 26, 22

3. What number am I?
   I have a 0 in the ones place.
   I am less than 400.
   The sum of my three numbers is 6.

   222, 321, 420, 330, 160

4. In a basketball contest, the team of Ian and Jacob throw 96 shots in 5 minutes. How many shots might each of them throw?

   70, 25, 65, 31, 55

Name ______________________________

14-5

Reteach

2NS2.0, 2NS6.0

Estimate Differences

Chapter Resources

About how many more miles is it from Chicago to Cleveland than from Chicago to Detroit?

Estimate 315 – 234.

From:	To:	Distance:
Chicago, IL	Cleveland, OH	315 miles
Chicago, IL	Detroit, MI	234 miles

Round to the nearest ten

Round 315 up to 320.
234 is closer to 230 than 240.

315 rounds to 320
– 234 rounds to – 230

The difference in miles is about ______ miles.

Round to the nearest hundred

315 is closer to 300 than 400.
234 is closer to 200 than 300.

315 rounds to 300
– 234 rounds to – 200

The difference in miles is about ______ miles.

---

			nearest ten		nearest hundred	exact
1.	687	⟶	690	⟶	700	687
	– 279	⟶	– 280	⟶	– 300	– 279
2.	571	⟶	570	⟶	600	571
	– 194	⟶	– 190	⟶	– 200	– 194

Name ___________________________

14-5

Skills Practice

2NS2.0, 2NS6.0

Estimate Differences

Round each number to the nearest *ten*. Estimate each difference.

1. 255 − 135   713 − 645   926 − 406   841 − 452

2. 501 − 398   488 − 216   377 − 164   667 − 325

3. **Round each number to the nearest *hundred*. Estimate each difference.**

487 − 244   705 − 280   376 − 111   947 − 321

Solve

4. Mae's family drives 467 miles on Saturday and 391 miles on Sunday. Rounding to the nearest ten, estimate the difference in miles.

____

5. Jake's school has a book sale every year. Last year, the school sold 209 books. They sell 311 books this year. Rounding to the nearest hundred, estimate the difference in books.

____

Name ______________________________

14-6

Reteach

2NS2.2, 2NS5.0

Subtract Money

Chapter Resources

Jim has $5.00. He buys the dog.
How much money does Jim have left?

$$\begin{array}{r} \$5.00 \\ -\ 2.35 \\ \hline \$2.65 \end{array}$$

Subtract. Show your work.

1. Pei-Li has $5.00. She buys the pig. How much money does she have left?

$5.00
– ___ . ___
___ . ___

2. Sami has $4.00. He buys the duck. How much money does he have left?

$4.00
– ___ . ___
___ . ___

3. Pam has $4.00. She buys the dog. How much money does she have left?

$4.00
– ___ . ___
___ . ___

4. $\begin{array}{r} \$4.74 \\ -\ 2.70 \\ \hline . \end{array}$ $\quad \begin{array}{r} \$6.99 \\ -\ 1.36 \\ \hline . \end{array}$ $\quad \begin{array}{r} \$5.25 \\ -\ 3.60 \\ \hline . \end{array}$

Name ______________________________

14-6

Skills Practice

2NS2.2, 2NS5.0

Subtract Money

Subtract.

1. $4.43 + 3.29 = ____ $7.28 − 1.19 = ____ $5.82 − 3.67 = ____ $6.16 − 2.46 = ____

2. $5.39 − 2.73 = ____ $3.63 − 1.47 = ____ $5.21 − 2.74 = ____ $9.97 − 5.80 = ____

3. $3.91 − 1.73 = ____ $8.25 − 0.18 = ____ $7.14 − 2.71 = ____ $4.29 − 3.07 = ____

Solve.

4. Tim has $6.85. He wants to buy a book for $3.58. He thinks he will still have enough money left to buy a magazine. Is Tim right? Explain your answer.

____

____

5. Lee has $4.87. His snack costs $3.56. If he buys his snack, does Lee still have $1.00 for the bus?

____

14-7

Name ___

Reteach (1)

2NS2.2, 2MR1.1

Problem-Solving Investigation: Choose a Strategy

Chapter Resources

Mia has 400 marbles. She gives some to her friend Nate. Mia has 200 marbles left. How many did she give to Nate?

Problem-Solving Strategies

- Use a Pattern
- Write a Number Sentence
- Use Logical Reasoning

Step 1
Understand

What do I know?

Mia has 400 marbles.
She gives away 200.

What do I need to find out?

How many she gives away.

Step 2
Plan

How will I find the number of marbles?

I will use write a number sentence. This will help me find the answer.

Step 3
Solve

Write a number sentence.

400 – 200 = 200

Nate has 200 marbles.

Step 4
Check

Look back.

Did I write the correct number sentence?

Name ______________________________

14-7

Reteach (2)

2NS2.2, 2MR1.1

Problem-Solving Investigation: Choose a Strategy

Problem-Solving Strategies
- Use a Pattern
- Write a Number Sentence
- Use Logical Reasoning

Solve.

1. There are 6 hundred, 5 tens, and 4 ones blocks. Tomas needs 3 hundred, 2 tens, and 4 ones blocks. How many blocks are left?

   ______ blocks

2. Tracy has 100 marbles. She gives away 1 on Monday. She gives away 2 marbles on Tuesday. She gives away 3 on Wednesday. If she continues to give away marbles at this rate, how many marbles will she have left after 1 week?

   ______ marbles

3. Mr. Patel has 237 animals at his pet store. There are 168 birds, gerbils, and hamsters. The rest of the animals are fish. Rounding to the nearest ten, estimate how many fish Mr. Patel has in his store.

   ______

   How many fish are actually there? ______

4. Tyrone has $4.00 to pay for lunch. If his lunch costs $2.87, how much money will Tyrone have left?

   ______

Name ______________________________

Skills Practice

2NS2.2, 2MR1.1

Problem-Solving Investigation: Choose a Strategy

Chapter Resources

Problem-Solving Strategies

- Use a Pattern
- Write a Number Sentence
- Use Logical Reasoning

Solve.

1. Mrs. Dahl has 9 hundred, 7 tens, and 8 ones blocks. Al borrows 2 hundreds, 5 tens, and 5 ones blocks. How many blocks are left?

   ______ blocks

2. Nell and Sam save 620 pennies. They put 372 pennies in a blue can. They put the rest in a red can. How many pennies do they put in the red can?

   ______ pennies

3. Mrs. Robbin's science class plants seeds. On Tuesday 2 seeds sprout. 4 sprout on Wednesday. 6 come up on Thursday. If the pattern continues, how many seeds will have sprouted on Friday in all?

   ______ seeds

4. Josh has $8.50 to buy a present for his dad. He spends $5.97 on the present. He spends another $1.00 for a big ribbon. How much money does Josh have left?

   ____